MW00604720

FUTUREPROOF
SUPPLY CHAIN

Planning for Disruption Risks
and Opportunities in the Lifeline
of the Global Economy

JASON SCHENKER

Copyright © 2019 Prestige Professional Publishing LLC

All rights reserved.

FUTUREPROOF SUPPLY CHAIN

Planning for Disruption Risks and Opportunities in the Lifeline of the Global Economy

BY JASON SCHENKER

No part of this publication may be reproduced, copied, stored in or transmitted into a data retrieval system, or transmitted in any form, or by any means (electronic, mechanical, photocopying, recording, or any other method) without written permission of the publisher, Prestige Professional Publishing LLC.

ISBN: 978-1-946197-26-9 *Paperback*
      978-1-946197-24-5 *Ebook*

For everyone working in our
supply chain.

CONTENTS

CONTENTS

CONTENTS

THE FUTURE OF SUPPLY CHAIN

Supply chain is the lifeblood of the global economy. Awareness about supply chain has increased in recent years, and its importance will only increase in the future.

During the 20th century, the notion of supply chain was largely only understood by practitioners within manufacturing firms. Even when I worked as an economist supporting a commodity trading desk in the early 2000s, and later at McKinsey building trading desks and designing hedging strategies, the words *supply chain* were seldom used.

But supply chain is no longer a concept that is relegated to a small corner of the manufacturing world.

The rise of e-commerce has thrown supply chain under the spotlight of the economy and retail sales. And the expectations of consumers related to supply chain will only increase. The line between wholesale, retail, and the consumer has become permanently blurred.

Consumers are now at the tail end of the supply chain. People have become accustomed to rapid fulfillment of their consumer needs, and their demands will increase over time. And the technology to fill those needs and meet those demands will rapidly change to meet rising demand.

Ever since I left McKinsey to found Prestige Economics in 2009, I have been deeply involved with supply chain topics, including conducting spend analysis, performing material handling industry forecasting, creating a material handling business activity index — or BAI — for MHI, and performing supply chain risk management analysis. And this book is based on consulting work that Prestige Economics and The Futurist Institute have done for Fortune 500 companies and industry groups.

I am excited to share my knowledge and experience of supply chain with you. And I get to do it within a futurist framework, based on the research of The Futurist Institute.

The main goals of *Futureproof Supply Chain* are to introduce you to the notion of how important technological developments have been for supply chain, and to share how new and emerging technological developments are likely to continue to impact supply chain dynamics.

This book has been carefully crafted to provide digestible explanations of complex concepts. To meet these goals, I have structured a mix of explanations, anecdotes, and graphics to provide context and relevance to what can be an otherwise daunting set of technology topics.

Acknowledgements

I want to acknowledge and thank all of the people who were involved in one way or another with the process of making this book come together. First, I want to thank **Nawfal Patel** and my other colleagues at The Futurist Institute and Prestige Economics who helped me bring this book to fruition.

Additionally, even though they did not participate in the production of this book, I wish to express my sincerest thanks to those individuals who have helped me in the field of supply chain! There are so many people who have helped me over the years.

At the top of the list is **Rob Handfield**, who runs the world-class Supply Chain Resource Cooperative (SCRC) at North Carolina State University. We have been doing work together for over a decade, and I have had both the honor and the privilege of being an occasional member of the SCRC Advisory Board since 2013. It is also through Rob that I got to know **Daniel Stanton,** who goes by the moniker Mr. Supply Chain. I am grateful that Daniel helped bring me deeper into the supply chain world when we came to know each other through the SCRC.

I also want to thank all of my amazing colleagues at **MHI**, the U.S. industry group for material handling industries. Prestige Economics has been working with MHI since 2014 to produce analyses, forecasts, and business activity reports for the material handling industry and specific material handling industry groups. I am especially grateful for support from MHI leadership, especially **George Prest**, **John Paxton**, and **Heather Taylor.**

I am also grateful to my former MHI colleagues **Matt Smurr** and **David Schwebel** for their support. David and many other amazing supply chain professionals have also worked with me on The Futurist Institute's work *The Robot and Automation Almanac*. I am grateful to all of our almanac contributors.

I also with to express my thanks to the **MHI members** and **SCRC members** who have generously helped expand my knowledge of supply chain and material handling over the years. Thank you so much!

As an economist, I firmly believe that my understanding of the global supply chain has been a tremendous edge in forecasting commodity prices, macroeconomic indicators, and central bank policy. Along those lines, I also want to thank **Jim Rice** of MIT, with whom I first became acquainted when I pursued my executive certificate at MIT's Center for Transportation and Logistics back in 2014. These MIT courses helped expand my knowledge and understanding of supply chain, transportation networks, and logistics challenges at the highest academic levels. And they have made me a more meticulous analyst of supply chain dynamics.

On a professional level, I want to acknowledge **Craig Fuller**, the CEO of Freightwaves. It has been a tremendous pleasure to work with him and his team. I greatly respect his big push to improve freight risk management by creating a solution with traded contracts. This is something that was until recently inconceivable, and the launch of these contracts in March 2019 could prove to be an immediate-term change of revolutionary proportions.

Finally, and most importantly, I want to thank my family for supporting me as I worked on this book. I am always most grateful for the support of my loving wife, **Ashley Schenker**, and to my parents, **Janet and Jeffery Schenker**.

My family has supported me in countless ways over the years by providing emotional support and editorial feedback.

Every time I write a book, it's a crazy experience that spills over into my family life, so to them and to everyone else who helped me in this process, thank you!

Finally, thank you for buying this book.

I hope you enjoy *Futureproof Supply Chain*!

~ Jason Schenker

BEING FUTUREPROOF: RISKS AND OPPORTUNITIES

The big idea of this book is that the supply chain has been at the forefront of technological changes in recent years and that it will continue to be so in the years ahead. This means that supply chain professionals and executives will need to be abreast of the latest new and emerging technologies if they want their companies — and their own careers — to be futureproof.

An efficient, rapid, and effective supply chain is now a conditio sine qua non for any successful business. It has become a core function and ingredient of profitability. And supply chain pressures are only likely to rise.

But technology isn't the only bugaboo that can rain on the future automated parade of global logistics and supply chain. Now more than ever, maintaining an edge in supply chain will be more critical. And that means being aware of any risks that can upset a highly streamlined, optimized, and engineered supply chain. Any company exposed to the risks of an increasingly integrated global supply chain will need to be aware of other major risks ahead if it wants to truly be futureproof.

In order to tackle the most important factors that will drive the future of supply chain, I have divided this book into eight sections:

- **Supply Chain: Vanguard of Disruption**
- **Computational Disruption and Opportunities**
- **Last Mile Disruptions and Solutions**
- **Economic Risks**
- **Market Risks and Opportunities**
- **Political Risks**
- **Staying Futureproof**
- **Pulling Everything Together**

In the first section of *Futureproof Supply Chain*, **Supply Chain: Vanguard of Disruption**, I discuss the importance of supply chain in the economy in Chapter 2, and I discuss the dynamics of recent disruptive technology dynamics that have impacted supply chain in Chapter 3. I also discuss why I wrote this book in Chapter 1.

In the second section, **Computational Disruption and Opportunities**, I discuss some of the most important current, new, and emerging computational trends that will have significant implications for supply chain. I discuss the internet of things — IoT — and sensors in Chapter 4 as well as machine learning and AI in Chapter 5. Then, I discuss the prospects of increased automation, which is dependent on hardware and software, in Chapter 6. I also discuss blockchain in Chapter 7 and quantum computing in Chapter 8.

The third section of the book includes my discussion of **Last Mile Disruptions**. This is one of the most important parts of the book, because last mile issues are going to become increasingly critical for supply chain professionals as e-commerce continues to expand. In Chapter 9, I present an overview of last mile issues. Then, in Chapter 10, I discuss self-driving vehicles, and in Chapter 11, I discuss drones. In Chapter 12, I address the disruptive potential supply chain impact of 3D printing.

In the fourth section of the book, I discuss **Economic Risks**. These come from two distinct areas: demographics and entitlements. While risks associated with the graying of the population are often looked at as a critical issue in the United States, it is a global problem that countries in Europe, Asia, and the rest of the world will need to attend to. In China, for example, the issues associated with a narrower population pyramid could present challenges to human-driven economic and productivity growth in the future. Entitlement risks are addressed in Chapter 13, and demographics are the subject of discussion in Chapter 14.

In the fifth section, **Market Risks and Opportunities**, I discuss the future of finance, including the financialization of markets as well as digital currencies. The elevated market risks posed by an accelerated financialization of markets present heightened operational financial risks as currencies, commodities, equities, and interest rates fluctuate with increased automation and synchronicity. This is the subject of Chapter 15. In Chapter 16, I address the topic of digital currencies, looking at both the hype and the hope in light of developments in 2017 and 2018.

The sixth section of *Futureproof Supply Chain* is titled **Political Risks**; I discuss the rise of nationalism as an anti-globalization ideology as well as the risk of new nations being born out of secession movements in Chapter 17. In Chapter 18, I discuss trade risks, which are particularly relevant given the global trade dynamics of the past year. In Chapter 19, I discuss privacy risks, and as an extension of that topic, I discuss cybersecurity and other security topics in Chapter 20.

In this book's seventh section, **Staying Futureproof**, I discuss the importance of having a futureproof organization — and of having a futureproof career by being a futureproof supply chain professional. I illustrate how to incorporate new and emerging technology risks and opportunities into your strategic planning in Chapter 21. This topic is extended in Chapter 22, which discusses the plan to build an internal corporate futurist practice.

Finally, in Chapter 23, I discuss individual strategies to be futureproof. This chapter includes critical suggestions on how to build skills, advance your career, and get buy-in on new technology ideas in order to ensure your career can ride the wave of technology ahead.

In the eighth and last section of this book, **Pulling Everything Together**, I tie in the technological changes ahead with futureproof strategies to present some important actionable recommendations for corporate, industry, professional, and individual implications. I also share some other forward-looking futurist thoughts as part of the book's conclusion.

In sum, the eight sections of this book should help you understand the most important new and emerging technologies for the United States and global supply chains. Furthermore, this book imparts practical strategies that you can implement immediately to make sure you, your team, and your company stay ahead of the competition by embracing technology.

Supply Chain:
Vanguard of Disruption

CHAPTER 1

WHY I WROTE THIS BOOK

I wrote this book to help individuals learn about some of the new and emerging disruptive technologies that will be critical for the future of supply chain. How we consume, how we manufacture, and how we process data are all going to be driven by relentless rising needs of consumers. I wanted to share what I know and have experienced in a way that could help prepare others for what comes next.

I am particularly pleased to have been able to incorporate my experiences in supply chain, financial market, and industry analysis that I have aggregated from advising corporate clients, industry groups, boards, and executives about recent supply chain developments, as well as future risks and opportunities.

This book is a collection of insights that I have shared with numerous clients and industry groups in recent years. In hindsight, I should have written this book years ago, but I have been busy building up and establishing the courses at The Futurist Institute.

Of course, many of the topics in this book have been cornerstones of The Futurist Institute's FLTA— Futurist and Long-Term Analyst — certification and training program. I simply did not have the time to craft a work that examined so many new technologies with explicit supply chain implications.

In the second half of 2018, however, I realized that The Futurist Institute had created so much research that it was time to codify the futurist implications of new and emerging technologies for supply chain activities, industries, professions, and individuals.

This realization kicked off a publishing frenzy in September 2018, and I have since published one book per month. My goal is to do this for 12 months in a row. This is book No. 6.

And why am I the one to write this book?

My background as an economic and financial professional has included several master's degrees as well as graduate-level courses in economics, finance, and accounting as part of my Master's in Applied Economics and part of an MBA. Plus, I hold a certificate from MIT's Center for Transportation and Logistics.

As for my work experience, I have advised executives on supply chain topics for over a decade at The Futurist Institute and Prestige Economics, and less explicitly at McKinsey and Wachovia, before it became Wells Fargo.

In this book, you'll learn about 15 new and emerging disruptive dynamics that will rock supply chains in the decade ahead.

It's important to know what these new and emerging technologies are — and how they work.

But don't worry — we won't be doing crazy math in this book.

In this book, we will also look at how your company, your profession, and you personally can be futureproof. This is important because it isn't just important to know what supply chain dynamics are changing and how they will impact your business or job. It is also important to know how to stay ahead of these new and emerging risks — as well as future risks that will crop up at an ever-increasing pace.

In short, you'll know how to spot new technology risks and opportunities as they emerge. And you will learn a framework for addressing those risks and capturing the upside opportunities.

That is really why I wrote this book: to help people understand the technological changes that have happened, are on the verge of happening, and could happen next for supply chains.

With that in mind, let's dive in!

CHAPTER 2

SUPPLY CHAIN IN THE ECONOMY

Supply chain, logistics, and material handling are critical activities in the economy that have long been taken for granted. But with the rise of e-commerce, they have been pushed to the limits. And supply chain has been pushed to the forefront of consumer activity.

The reason is simple: the promise of e-commerce has an enticing lure of convenience. In economies like the United States, where consumption is around 70 percent of all economic activity, e-commerce is on the rise — both in dollar terms and as a percent of total retail sales.

And the upside potential for increased importance of supply chain solutions to meet the needs of an impatient consumer economy is massive. The demand of business and e-commerce has long exceeded what humans working in the physical supply chain could do by themselves. And this dynamic has driven supply chain use of automated solutions, robotics, and improved software solutions.

The most recent data available for retail sales in the United States shows a very strong trend of growth in the dollar value of online sales and e-commerce. You can see this dollarized growth in e-commerce in Figure 2-1.

But this trend isn't being driven by price pressures from inflation. This is a trend being driven by a secular move away from brick-and-mortar retail, in a trend that for many years has often been typified by the phrase "from bricks to clicks."

This is, in part, why some have called restaurants the new retail. Because warehouses and distribution centers are effectively the new retail, and your phone is effectively the kiosk interface with which you execute your purchase.

Figure 2-1: Value of E-Commerce Retail Sales[1]

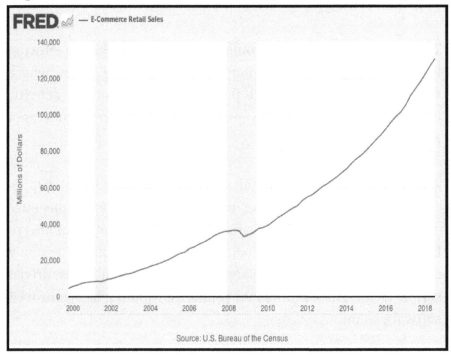

Of course, the rise of e-commerce retail sales as a percent of total retail sales has also been rising too. In Figure 2-2, you can see the up-and-to-the-right trend of e-commerce strength.

In the fourth quarter of 1999, U.S. e-commerce sales were already at $4.5 billion. By the third quarter of 2018, data showed that e-commerce retail sales had risen to $130.9 billion. But there is still a lot more potential for e-commerce sales to grow in both absolute terms and as a percent of total retail sales.

After all, back in the fourth quarter of 1999, e-commerce represented just 0.6 percent of total retail sales. And even in the third quarter of 2018, e-commerce retail sales were still below 10 percent — at just 9.8 percent of all retail sales.

Figure 2-2: E-Commerce Retail as a Percent of Total Sales[2]

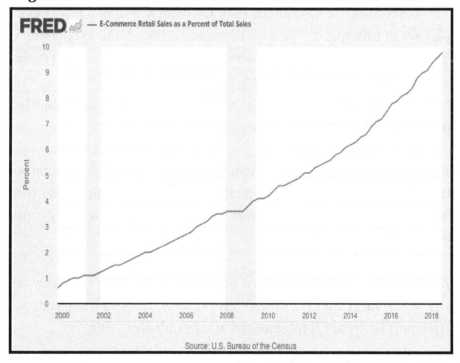

This relatively low percentage of total retail sales is lower than most people might expect because many items like fuel, cars, and food have ben historically more difficult to obtain online. But there are countless startups — as well as larger, more established firms — that are working to expand the reach of e-commerce into every nook and cranny of retail.

Amazon's move into Whole Foods has been just one of countless emerging pushes into grocery delivery. A number of supermarket chains have also created or acquired firms specializing in delivery services. Plus, there are many companies focused on delivering meals, like Blue Apron and Hello Fresh. Of course, not all of these tech solutions will survive. But the notion that people would never buy groceries online is long dead.

The same could be said about cars. Carvana is one of a few major players in this space. The idea of buying a car online may seem a bit sketchy to those of us who might be called "olds" (read: anyone over 30). But one of the least pleasant things many people do in their lives is to go buy and, more importantly, negotiate the price of a new or used car.

While vehicle sales may remain more resistant to e-commerce than other purchases, some consumers will inevitably ride the e-commerce wave into the driver's seat of a car they will use only about 5 percent of the time.

And that brings me to one final point about cars. We are likely to see fewer individually owned vehicles, once self-driving vehicle transport fleets are implemented and readily available.

Once we see a rise in fleet vehicle purchases of cars to meet self-driving automated transport needs, this will have a significant impact on the calculation of retail sales. And we will likely see reclassification of larger percentages of vehicle sales as business investment line items in quarterly GDP reports.

In reality, this could increase the importance of investment as a percent of GDP while decreasing the personal consumption expenditures component. The change will not flip the numbers totally, since personal consumption is about 70 percent of GDP and business investment is 15 percent of GDP. But vehicles are not cheap. And self-driving vehicles of the future will be more expensive, further skewing the impact on business investment expenditures.

This could push up investment (as a percent of GDP) by several percentage points or more, while having the inverse impact on personal consumption expenditures. The most important takeaway here is that the changes in which people consume, the rise of e-commerce, and the compressing of the supply chain will impact everything from business models to official releases of economic data.

At some point, many of the economic data series we are accustomed to looking at are likely to see significant changes and could experience tectonic-level shifts. One area where we have already seen this is in the jobs figures for U.S. department store retail jobs, as well as the job series for warehousing and storage, which are supply chain jobs.

In Figure 2-3, you can see the sharp decline in department store retail jobs since 2000. This drop-off in jobs coincides with the time period during which e-commerce has been rising in absolute dollars and as a percent of total retail sales. Essentially, fewer people have been needed to work retail in department stores as consumers have eschewed the hodgepodge collection of departments in favor of specialty stores and online retail.

Interesting to note is the word in the title of the graph in parenthesis and all caps: "DISCONTINUED." In fact, after experiencing a massive loss of about half a million jobs from its peak in mid-2001, this series was discontinued in December 2017.

Figure 2-3: Department Store Retail Jobs[3]

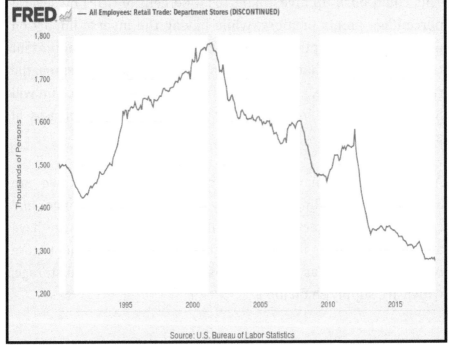

In stark contrast to department store retail jobs is a data series that has most certainly not been discontinued. It is the number of transportation and warehousing jobs in the subcategory of warehousing and storage. In Figure 2-4, you can see the growth of these e-commerce jobs that have been created in the supply chain to meet consumer demand.

Since mid-2001, this data series has shown an increase of around 700,000 jobs. This is important because it speaks to the question of whether automation destroys or creates jobs. Throughout human history, automation and robots have allowed people to do more with the aid of technology.

Some people say this time is different. But I doubt it.

Figure 2-4: Warehousing and Storage Jobs[4]

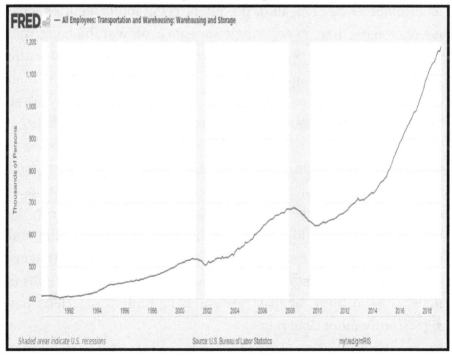

The first thing to realize is that the number of new warehousing and storage jobs created since 2001 exceeds the number of lost department store retail sales jobs by 200,000 jobs. Furthermore, the warehousing and storage jobs are better-paying jobs.

The jobs created by historically unimaginable consumer demand that has pressured the global supply to adapt to single-piece batching rather than palette shipments has created good jobs. In Figure 2-5, you can see different categories of retail sales jobs and their respective wages. And in Figure 2-6, you can see the different categories of warehousing and storage jobs and their mean hourly wages as well.

The most important takeaway here is that warehousing and storage jobs pay more than retail jobs. In fact, with the exception of automobile dealers, all of the major retail job categories have lower wages than every single category of warehousing and storage jobs. Furthermore, the mean retail hourly wage for the most expensive category of retail sales workers (other than automobile dealers) is still cheaper than the mean hourly wage for the cheapest category of warehousing and storage workers.

Clearly, the expansion of the supply chain hasn't just been good for consumers or for companies in logistics and automation. It has also had positive net impacts on the U.S. workforce, by creating jobs in the higher-paying category of warehousing and storage, compared to where jobs were lost in the lower-paying area of department store retail sales. Although the loss of jobs is never a good thing, at least warehousing and storage jobs pay significantly more than retail.

Figure 2-5: Pay Scale of Retail Jobs[5]

Industry	Employment (1)	Percent of industry employment	Hourly mean wage	Annual mean wage (2)
General Merchandise Stores	838,540	26.04	$11.58	$24,090
Clothing Stores	747,000	70.22	$11.98	$24,920
Building Material and Supplies Dealers	416,700	36.96	$14.06	$29,240
Sporting Goods, Hobby, and Musical Instrument Stores	302,150	56.26	$11.57	$24,060
Automobile Dealers	275,740	21.39	$21.50	$44,720

Figure 2-6: Pay Scale of Warehousing and Storage Jobs[6]

Data series	Wages, 2017			
	Hourly		Annual	
	Median	Mean	Median	Mean
Industrial truck and tractor operators	16.43	16.99	34,180	35,340
Laborers and freight, stock, and material movers, hand	14.28	15.12	29,710	31,450
Shipping, receiving, and traffic clerks	15.28	16.36	31,780	34,020
Stock clerks and order fillers	14.90	15.76	31,000	32,790
Transportation, storage, and distribution managers	43.21	45.57	89,870	94,780

CHAPTER 3

TECHNOLOGY AND SUPPLY CHAIN

The recent and future economic impact of e-commerce cannot be understated. And none of it would have happened without supply chain adoption of technology that has allowed for the compression of the global supply chain and the extension of the supply chain directly into our in-hand devices.

These developments also mean that supply chains are no longer responsive to the orders of a few major store chains, or even thousands of smaller stores. This change means that e-commerce will continue to be driven by the whims of a mass of individual consumers. And while consumers may sometimes behave irrationally and erratically, one thing you can always count on is their impatience.

The need for technology to short-circuit the impatience of consumers cannot be understated. Advances in new technology will significantly impact how supply chains function operationally in the coming decade — and well into the future. Consumers have forced supply chain to the forefront of technological innovation.

Computational Disruptions and Opportunities

CHAPTER 4

INTERNET OF THINGS
AND SENSORS

One of the most critical emerging technologies that will impact the way the United States and global supply chains operate in the coming decade will be the rise of the internet of things, otherwise known as IoT. The term *IoT* is thrown around a lot, and it generally refers to the increased connectivity of physical items to the internet.

Currently, we have the internet of phones, tablets, and computers.

When we have full IoT, we will have the internet of cars, refrigerators, supply closets, and all kinds of industrial, commercial, and personal-use items that will be connected to the internet. Furthermore, these items won't be functioning as WiFi hotspots for phones, tables, and computers.

These devices will connect to the internet in order to perform their primary functions. Through the use of sensors and this connectivity, these devices will act *independently* to perform certain tasks — like order parts, goods, or services online. These are often called "smart" things.

IoT at Home

Food and household items may be provided through long-term continuous agreements. This would make buying groceries, office supplies, car parts, and other items similar to the continuous service that is codified in something like a cellphone plan.

For example, a "smart refrigerator" owner might set up a certain milk for automated reorder, which could be in place for the entire 10-year life of the appliance. The terms of the agreement could be set with the purchase of the refrigerator, and ending the contract for the 10-year period may require a buyout fee that another brand of milk may be willing to pay.

If we consider the milk agreement from the supply side, milk vendors might offer deals to get you to buy their milk at the time a refrigerator is purchased. This could be like power, cable, or internet companies that offer sign-up deals at the time of a new apartment rental. Another example, of course, would be like cellphone contracts that offer a certain level of data usage per month.

Of course, if you lock into one milk vendor, this would be good for the incumbent. But it could present competitive challenges for new market entrants of smaller vendors. In our milk example, if a milk vendor wants to get new customers, it may have to offer one year of free milk to get you to switch vendors for the life of the fridge.

Your fridge may begin showing you advertisements for related products.

By the way, this could work for eggs, vegetables, meats, and any other food your family may need.

It may be the case that a fridge and food plan may be implemented with guaranteed levels of inventory at the home of the refrigerator owner. This could help the vendor plan, and with increased IoT data access into homes, essentially the supply chain would extend all the way into individuals' kitchens.

Business Examples of IoT

In addition to household items, you could also see IoT impact business operations. This could make the purchase of all business items become like agreements for heavy equipment.

The cost of a commercial vehicle purchase combined with the cost of replacement parts and maintenance is referred to as TCO — or total cost of ownership — in the procurement world. It is a calculation that is very important for businesses. Inertia and permanence of service agreements increasingly become parts of sales agreements for machinery and equipment.

Companies could buy conveyers that automatically order replacement belts and gears or automatically schedule their own maintenance calls. Businesses may buy pens and paper from vendors for the life of a smart supply closet. It is the corporate equivalent of the IoT refrigerator.

As with the fridge, your supply closet may begin showing you advertisements for related products. And it may have long-term agreements with buyout clauses.

As you can see, in a world dominated by IoT, inanimate objects engage with the supply chain directly through their sensors and their connection to the internet.

In many ways, the things become the end user and customer. Sensors are required to trigger orders or actions, while internet connectivity makes execution possible. But it is all likely to rest on prescribed vendor-customer relationships

I've given a number of examples here already, but consider some examples of the kinds of devices, like the refrigerator and the supply closet, that will connect to the internet to perform their primary device functions.

Figure 4-1: An IoT Fridge.[1]

Another example would be a car that orders its own replacement parts as part of an agreement that is signed when the car is purchased. Or consider the potential for a copy machine to schedule its own repairman to visit in line with its purchase and service agreement.

There are many different ways that we will see IoT manifest itself, and it will make things a lot more convenient for consumers. But it will also have a number of critical impacts on the way supply chains operate and how companies interact with their real — or inanimate — customers.

Let's look at some of these potential impacts on supply chain.

Figure 4-2: The Internet of Phones, Laptops, and Tablets.[2]

Disruptive Impacts of IoT on Supply Chains

As with all things, the move to a more fully integrated IoT supply chain will be a mix of positive and negative factors. As I've already alluded to, the biggest reason IoT will happen is that it will make life easier and more pleasant for consumers.

Mundane and often annoying tasks, like buying groceries, ordering office supplies, or taking your car to get an oil change, will be a thing of the past. These tasks, which have long been in the shallow end of the pool of task drudgery, will now be relegated to machines.

But they will not be without cost.

SaaS Income Absorption

Consumers may not notice the costs, due to what one of my clients likes to call "income absorption." The move to software as a service — or SaaS — models of doing business has worked well for business-to-business as well as business-to-customer operations. People pay a small amount per the agreement over time, and they don't notice the cost.

Think of a gym membership you may have forgotten about for a year, or a certain software program you didn't realize you've been paying an annual renewal on since 2015.

Although these IoT agreements may go largely unnoticed, they are likely to prove quite profitable for the companies that use them to lock in customers. At some point, there may be consumer backlash. But I doubt it. SaaS is here to stay.

Supply Chain Implications

One of the positive impacts of an IoT world for vendors is that once a company is set up as a vendor, the customer relationship is almost permanent. As noted above, SaaS relationships involve an almost imperceptible level of costs, so that cancelling those relationships is unlikely.

This is good for the vendors who secure such agreements. It means their customer relationships could prove very long-lived. And it would make sales volumes and cash flow more stable and predictable. Plus, it could make forecasting demand easier as well, reducing inventories and waste. As an even bigger plus, it is quite likely that the price sensitivity of established customers could actually fall, insomuch as price increases may go unnoticed by customers. Or if they are noticed, it may not be enough of an issue to push them to sever their relationship.

Clearly, there are big benefits for companies that can secure IoT relationships. But there is one big problem: It would greatly favor market leaders and incumbent vendors.

Aside from the fact that customers would be locked into long-lived agreements that they would be unlikely to break, it may become much more difficult for a vendor to directly access the retail market. After all, if there is low price sensitivity of existing customers, it means that potential new customers would have to see a big financial incentive to break their long-term IoT agreements. Just think about how tough it would be to cancel your cellphone plan.

Or a gym membership.

It is particularly onerous. And it's intentionally set up that way.

Now, imagine if all of the things you own had agreements like a cellphone contract. How likely would you be to switch? Probably not very likely — at least not until it came time to buy a new IoT device that comes with a bundled package.

But even if you were to consider changing your milk agreements or pen agreements or whatnot, the chance of getting accidental exposure to new products or vendors is almost impossible. And for a company, this means that getting new customers will be very challenging. If all groceries are bought online in automated IoT agreements, you won't have the same level of accidental product discovery you have when walking through a supermarket today. Now, you might see a new product and decide to try it. But in the future, if everything is done IoT in fixed agreements, the products you even have the option to buy will be a much more curated list. And that will increase demand certainty for the vendor. But it will also decrease variety for you. And it could limit future competition.

With IoT there are potential benefits as well as risks ahead. But one thing seems likely: The companies that are well-established product incumbents with strong brand adherence will likely have even greater market power in an IoT world than they do today. And that's likely to be just as true for food as it is for office supplies, auto parts, and just about everything else.

CHAPTER 5

MACHINE LEARNING AND AI

There is an awful tendency among technology experts as well as futurists to use buzzwords. Those of us who are active in the technology world often refer to this as buzzword bingo.

Machine learning and AI are two of the terms that are part of most technology experts' jargon-stuffed card of bingo buzzwords.

Essentially, machine learning describes the ability for computer programs to learn binary decision making from exposure to large amounts of data, which are critical to establishing pattern recognition. Some people will also refer to this as predictive analytics.

But it does not matter if you call this technique to drive valuable, actionable, and potentially profitable implications from data machine learning or predictive analytics. Essentially, it is the same thing. And it is something that most people simply called statistics up until just a few years ago.

Machine Learning Conceptualization

Machine learning allows computer programs to recognize patterns, and it allows robots to perform tasks that require less structured actions with guidelines. Machine learning feeds into predictive analytics, insomuch as a program that has "learned" something can predict an outcome. This differs greatly from artificial intelligence, which is the level of computer programming and robotics, when software and robots can seek out patterns and make predictions without instructions or guidelines.

Machine Learning Examples

Let's look at a number of examples of machine learning. One classic example of machine learning, which has been savagely parodied by the TV show *Silicon Valley* is image identification. I once heard a partner at Andreesen Horowitz describe the ability for machine learning programs to determine the difference between a dog and not a dog by looking at 10,000 pictures.

Essentially, by having a human provide inputs, the program can begin to recognize patterns. But this does not mean that the computer program that can identify a dog or not a dog can create a dog. In fact, when some programs have been asked to do this, they have sometimes generated unusual images, like dogs with multiple heads, too many legs, or unusual shapes.

Another example of machine learning would be for a computer with a microphone to recognize your emotions by your intonation. As with the images, however, the computer would need inputs about emotions while recording intonations in order to predict emotions by intonation.

A similar example of machine learning would be a software program for email that can identify your mood by word choice. Or a software program that can identify important language related to a trial.

In a physical operation, a robot that has developed machine learning capabilities can put a pin in a hole, even if the hole is not in a prespecified place and the robot must find the hole. This is also done by exposing the machine to different experiences.

In supply chain, a machine learning program might look for inconsistencies in invoices, bills of lading, or defective units.

Figure 5-1: Computato ergo sum.[1]

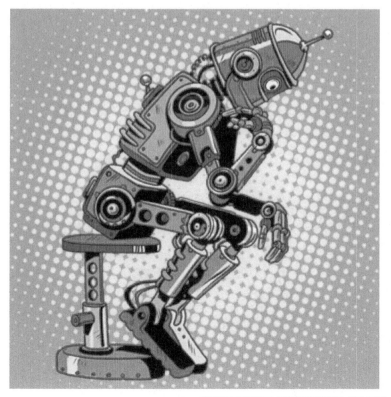

Artificial Intelligence

In stark contrast to human-guided input requirements of machine learning, artificial intelligence occurs when computers can make decisions independently. AI can recognize patterns, even when it has not been programed to evaluate data in explicit binary decision-making patterns.

Artificial intelligence can really only happen with exposure to massive amounts of data. Significant processing power is also critical. I will discuss this in greater length in Chapter 8, which is about quantum computing.

Figure 5-2: Not quite artificial intelligence.[2]

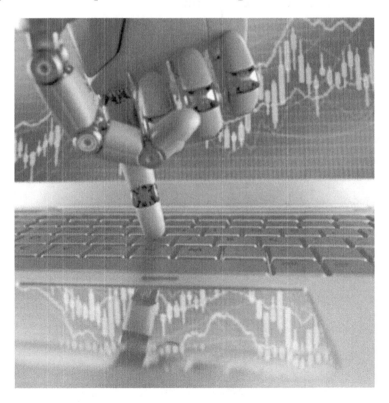

A prime example of emerging artificial intelligence is a self-driving car that can independently make decisions, based on microcalculations and almost unlimited probabilities of events that are updated frequently in milliseconds.

Another example, which is important for supply chain considerations, would be an IoT refrigerator that makes ordering decisions in an independently identified sequence rather than in a binary pattern. An example of this would be the IoT refrigerator ordering hot dog buns when hot dogs run out.

Disruptive Impacts on Supply Chains

As with other kinds of technology, there could be mixed impacts on supply chain from machine learning and artificial intelligence.

The big difference in how machine learning could be impactful versus how artificial intelligence could be impactful hinges on the parameters that are set. Machine learning usually will have set parameters to solve for, whereas artificial intelligence may just solve the problem rather than provide predictive analytics around these kinds of issues.

For example, given a massive set of transport data, an artificial intelligence program could independently optimize a supply chain, freight and fuel costs, or order volumes.

Even though these are positive potential developments that could be ushered in by machine learning and artificial intelligence, these advancements are unlikely to be without costs.

One cost would be that you could see technology replace some people who operate at very high skill levels. Additionally, you could see that programs may make independent decisions that offer the greatest shortcut without pricing in any other trade-offs, like bad press, stress to people on the job, or any kind of environmental or social impacts. The programs would likely be very efficient, but that does not mean they will make the best long-term or ethical choices.

Let's look at some examples of the upside potential and downside risks of machine learning and artificial intelligence in a future supply chain world.

Be Careful What You Wish For

For example, computer programs may choose vendors on completely objective measures of performance. Of course, specifying the prioritized data for consideration will have to be a parameter set by the customer. But if the customer does not include a data set with proper parameters, then the outcome could be unintended and disappointing.

An example would be if the AI system chooses to optimize vendor selection only by cost. In that case, you might get vendors that provide the lowest rock-bottom prices. But these vendors may also provide largely poor-quality goods or goods that are delivered late with great frequency.

Yes, the AI got the cheapest deal — but maybe not the best one all around.

Another example of how machine learning and artificial intelligence could disrupt supply chains would be with advertising that is purchased by algorithms.

This is another area where you would have to make sure that the AI parameters are properly set by a human. After all, if you tell the AI software that you want the ads to get the most traffic, you might find your ads on a site that caters to the wrong demographic, is in the wrong region, or is on a site that provides an ethical or moral conflict for the company.

For computer programs, there are a few things that always ring true. First, when working with a software program and a problem is given, the shortest path to the answer will be used. One example AI ethics advocates like to invoke is the notion that if we asked an AI to simply make the environment cleaner, it might decide humans are the problem and wipe us all out.

It would get the job done — but not in a way any of us would be particularly happy with. This is really just another way of saying garbage in, garbage out.

By that I mean that if the data in the process isn't good, the results won't be either. And the same could also be said for setting analytical parameters. If the parameters are misspecified, then the outcome will be suboptimal at best.

But if you have the right data and you set the right parameters, the benefits could be enormous.

Predicting is Easier

Despite potential drawbacks, there are major potential benefits of machine learning that could be positively disruptive for supply chain because predictive supply chain analytics will become easier.

This could be everything from predicting returns to predicting timing of orders or deliveries, and it could even be used to predict the most likely points of disruption in a supply chain over time, with regard to the exact time of year, season, weather, or any other factors. With machine learning, any potential number of factors could be optimized, any number of risks could be addressed, and any potential opportunities could be captured.

And in an AI format, a supply chain could be programmed to preemptively address these kind of risks and challenges.

Other Machine Learning and Artificial Intelligence Uses

As we look ahead 10 years, there are a number of other impacts that machine learning and artificial intelligence are likely to have on supply chains beyond predictive analytics and optimization of supply chain activities.

There is also likely to be increased uses of robotics and automation in supply chains that further accelerate the dispatch of goods. In fact, this is one of the critical topics that was reiterated by several of the contributors to *The Robot and Automation Almanac — 2019*. It seems as if robotics has come a long way. But AI software needs to catch up for there to be a further step change in efficiency and optimization.

Over the next decade, AI will also become a critical ingredient for self-driving vehicle fleets. This is likely to be one of the most critical changes to transportation and supply chain in history. But it requires real AI. After all, self-driving cars and other self-driving vehicles make adaptive movements with microcalculations in unstructured situations in order to achieve the best outcome with the highest probability of success.

I discuss this further in Chapter 10.

Once self-driving vehicle fleets are launched, I expect that we are likely to see on-road inventory. Essentially, some self-driving trucks on the roads will operate as de facto miniwarehouses on wheels. A master system would use data to predict where goods will be needed for instantaneous delivery, and these goods could be located nearby, making other deliveries but holding inventory on board in anticipation of certain orders. Of course, this kind of system would be highly efficient if it could be integrated with IoT devices.

There are countless other ways that analyzing the mountains of supply chain data will yield increases of efficiency, timeliness, and profitability. But this will all be done to satisfy impatient and demanding individual end consumers.

As in other industries, machine learning and AI will be used to squeeze profitability out of a system that will be forced to get leaner, meaner, and quicker over time. Quantum computing is eventually going to be a part of that equation, which is the subject of Chapter 8.

CHAPTER 6

INCREASED AUTOMATION

Automation will be a critical key to the success of supply chain activities in the years ahead. The current demands of e-commerce could not be met with people alone, and current e-commerce retail sales represent only 9.8 percent of all U.S. retail sales as of the third quarter of 2018. As supply chain needs grow, automation will increase as well.

All parts of the U.S. supply chain will require increased levels of automation to deal with increased burdens of single-piece retail demand for goods. Fortunately, the U.S. supply chain exists largely in two-dimensional space — or at least it does inside warehouses and distribution centers. And this is where we will need to draw a line when we talk about automated technology.

There is automated tech that we have seen deployed across the supply chain inside warehouses and distribution centers. This has been done, it will be done further, and it will continue to be a highly effective means of fulfilling the promise of e-commerce. But it is only one piece of the automation puzzle.

There is also a significant need for automated solutions to take goods out of factories, warehouses, and distribution centers and to bring them to consumers. This also includes last mile issues, which I will discuss further in Chapter 9.

On the delivery side of the supply chain, you are likely to see drones, self-driving vehicles, and other automated means of transport deliver industrial, commercial, or consumer goods. This could include flocks of large industrial drones working together to deliver heavy industrial equipment to remote sites.

But no matter what part of the supply chain we talk about, in the future the one thing that appears very likely is that more of the supply chain will be automated. And automation will be used with accelerating frequency in repetitive, predictive, and dangerous jobs.

There are a number of different kinds of automation you might see in practice. For example, you may see robots working not just at the largest warehouses and distribution centers, but they may also be doing all of the picking and packing at small facilities as well. Essentially, you are likely to see robotic proliferation across the supply chain — especially as software and hardware improve and costs fall.

And you are likely to see more robots used in construction of buildings — as well as in scrap metal processing. This means that the post-consumption supply chain is also likely to be increasingly automated as well.

Disruptive Impacts on Supply Chains

As with the other areas of development, automation technology presents mostly upside potential — but it still comes with some downside risks.

On the upside, automation increases efficiencies and the speed of goods movement. It also increases the ability to manufacture or deliver goods that were previously complicated or expensive to deliver. And automation can also ensure more stable and predictive delivery of industrial, commercial, and retail goods. Between the mix of increased speed, convenience, and predictability, it should be clear that the increased deployment of automation is likely to reduce delivery costs and increase profitability.

But there are a couple of downside risks posed to supply chains by automation as well. Most importantly, not all companies will have the same capital to invest to make the transition from the information age to the automation age. And preparing for a transition to the automation age requires significant capital investment on the part of companies. This means that there will be winners and losers. Companies that make the right investments will be the ones that capture a greater potential of upside in the future. And the adoption of more rapid automation solutions is likely to have a compounding impact on profits.

One other risk to consider is that between 2.2 and 3.1 million transportation jobs in the United States are likely to be lost due to automation. Other jobs lie ahead, but these losses could have a substantially negative impact on many individuals and society.

CHAPTER 7

BLOCKCHAIN

Blockchain is famous for being the technology behind the digital currency Bitcoin. And I will discuss the topic of digital currencies in Chapter 16.

But blockchain has an even higher-value use case. You see, blockchain technology presents tremendous opportunities for supply chain because it is essentially a multiparty verification database and distributed record keeping. In short, it is accounting software that works really well in trusted groups of parties that do frequent transactions — like in a supply chain of trusted parties.

Before we dig too deeply into the use cases of blockchain in supply chain, let's take a brief look at some of the key components of a blockchain — and how the technology works. You can see the parts in Figure 7-1. In the image, you see there are three parts of a blockchain: an individual record, a block of records, and a chain of blocks.

Each transaction is a **record**, whether we are talking about the transfer of a Bitcoin, a physical transport load, or a piece of property. There is a buyer and a seller, and this transaction is part of an individual record.

The record then becomes part of a **block** of transactions. That's the *block* in the word *blockchain*. These records of transactions in the block are processed together as a block. Then they are added to a chain of previously processed blocks.

Figure 7-1: Anatomy of a Blockchain

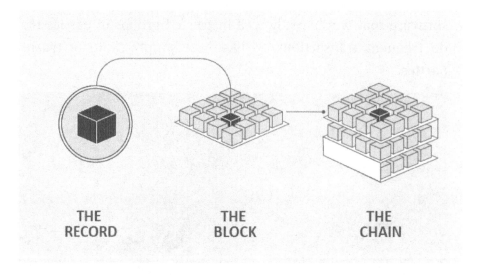

THE
RECORD

THE
BLOCK

THE
CHAIN

The **chain** in the word *blockchain* refers to the entire history of the blocks of processed records. This history — the entire blockchain — is then distributed as a ledger to its network.

These are the parts of a blockchain: records, blocks, and chain.

Now, it is also important to know that a blockchain works best in a distributed network of parties. In Figure 7-2, you can see what a distributed network looks like. It's when you have a number of different parties engaging in transactions and there is no central organization to the nature of these transactions. This is like what happens with multiple logistics and transport businesses that are transacting at different parts of a supply chain and with different parties. You have independence of actions and no natural central repository for all records.

Figure 7-2: A Distributed Network

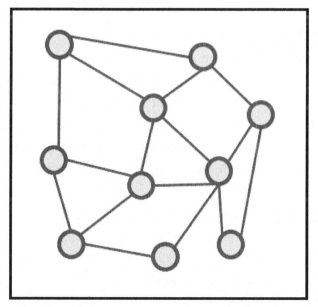

Conceptualization

As I mentioned at the beginning of this chapter, blockchain is essentially a multiparty verification system for transactions that requires parties outside of the transaction itself to verify the parties of the transaction and the actual transaction itself. These transactions occur in blocks, and since there is a chain of transactions in blocks, these have the ability to be traced on a distributed ledger among select parties with access to that ledger.

Essentially, it is a distributed database of accounting software that has a strong value proposition for supply chain entities.

The potential for blockchain to add economic value in many different industries and corporate fields is significant. But it isn't equal across industries. The biggest value proposition is where there are supply chains and risks to mitigate, as well as health and safety issues.

Assets in Transition See Greatest Use Case

The value proposition for using blockchains for record keeping on long-lived assets is lower than for assets that move. This is true whether we are talking about financial assets that frequently move between investments, markets, and parties — or assets that physically move or are in flux. This impacts The Futurist Institute's assessment for blockchain use potential in Figure 7-3.

In addition to movement factors driving the use case and value proposition for blockchain, there are limitations on blockchain's potential uses in some industries due to incumbent regulatory requirements and legal frameworks.

This is why healthcare, property, and government data uses for blockchain may prove more limited than for agricultural products, transport and logistics, and financial services.

The reason it is important to discuss blockchain in this book is because it is likely to be an important technology that is adopted for use by a number of companies in supply chain, transport, logistics, and material handling industries.

Blockchain may die on the vine for a number of industries, but for transport and logistics, blockchain is likely to be important. And this has everything to do with something economists call *transactional friction.*

Figure 7-3: Assessment of Blockchain Potential

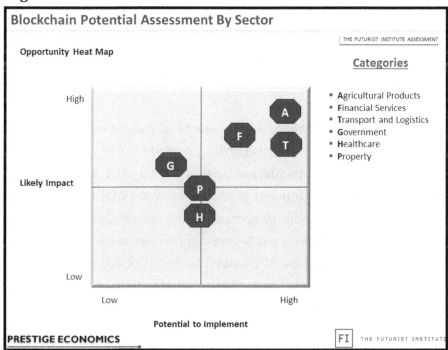

Transactional friction refers to the costs of doing business — and most specifically of doing physical transactions. This often refers to paperwork, legal documents, and expenses required to facilitate the trade, physical movement, and exchange of goods. These kinds of costs are ubiquitous in transport and logistics industries. And it's the reason why there is such a high value for blockchain in transport, logistics, and freight.

These are ideal industries for blockchain use because blockchain provides a distributed record that be can be set within a predefined network to ease and reduce that transactional friction. Basically, it would make the transport and exchange of goods faster, easier, and cheaper.

As in the field of finance, transactions in transport, logistics, and freight are frequent. This stands in stark contrast to the transfer of physical properties. And it ties back to my contention that the greatest potential use case and source of value for blockchain will be in industries where there is a high number of transactions.

Furthermore, like finance, some aspects of freight and transport are regulated. This is true regarding manufacturing restrictions of use on some chemicals as well as on conflict metals. Plus, counterfeiting is a significant problem for some high-value goods in the supply chain, like pharmaceuticals, certain manufactured goods like inverted delta parts, and military weaponry. And there are also high tech goods, like smartphones. Blockchain use could increase transparency in these supply chains, reducing potential fraud, increasing safety, and saving companies money.

The Futurist Institute identified nine different potential use cases for blockchain in transport and logistics. We expect that a number of these will drive blockchain use in transport over the coming decade.

The nine areas of high-potential use cases in transportation and logistics are:

Freight Tracking   **Trade Customs & Duties**
Chain of Custody   **Conflict Minerals**
Local Content   **Restricted Chemicals**
Restricted Agriculture   **Pharma Tracking**
Intellectual Property

Figure 7-4: Assessment of Blockchain Potential in Transport

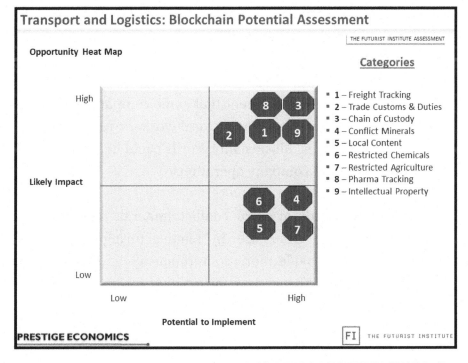

So what do each of these mean? And how could a blockchain actually be applied to each of these challenge areas of supply chain? Well, let's look at each of these.

Freight Tracking would include a distributed record of where vehicles have been that is part of the ledger and record.

Trade Customs & Duties would include a digital and permanent record of international trade, tariff, and duties records.

Chain of Custody would be the integrated digital record of goods and a complete and permanent record of their locations.

Conflict Minerals are restricted from trade and use in goods manufacturing by countries due to their social impact, illegal nature, or other criminal nature. Blockchain chain of custody records would make it more difficult for conflict minerals to enter the global supply chain.

Local Content is the requirement that some companies produce a certain percentage of goods using local workers, raw materials, goods, and/or services. Blockchain records could help track local content provisions of company operations.

Restricted Chemicals are like conflict minerals inasmuch as they are restricted from use in manufacturing operations. Blockchain could provide more comprehensive and permanent digital records that enhance and ensure restricted-chemicals-use compliance.

Pharma Tracking would ensure a comprehensive record of pharmaceutical product, which can be both high-value and critical for the physical well-being of the populace.

Intellectual Property refers to the ability for blockchain to provide a permanent, distributed, and digital record of the transport of high-value intellectual property goods, including military, high-tech dual use, and high-value consumer goods.

Restricted Agriculture is one final category for consideration, and it is already at the forefront of blockchain adoption. In The Futurist Institute's analysis, we noted agriculture as the highest-potential industry use case for blockchain. And this is primarily because agricultural foodstuffs are critical. And they are often subject to costly, wasteful, and deadly contaminations.

Blockchain in Practice
Here are few examples of some things you might see in supply chain with the broader adoption of blockchain technology:

- Tin import origins, which are critical for conflict mineral compliance, are verified with blockchain records.
- European Union blockchain records of imports of chemicals are digitally audited to be compliant with EU regulations for restricted chemicals.
- Transactions that currently require legal agreements, lengthy documentation, and maybe even physical paperwork are completed and verified with a click on your phone.
- Your own business activities can be more accurately monitored due to distributed ledger access within your organization.

Disruptive Impacts

As we think about the disruptive impacts of blockchain on supply chain, there are a few big positive elements to consider, including lower costs for physical transactions, record keeping, accounting, and legal documentation. Plus, there is the potential for more transparency for sourced materials.

But there are some downside risks as well. For the moment, blockchains can be complicated and costly to establish. In coming years, this cost is likely to fall dramatically. But one additional downside to consider is that blockchain is still imperfect if the people in the system are dishonest. And there are still risks of hacking. This is actually a big risk because the attack surface of a blockchain actually increases with a distributed ledger.

One Caveat About Fraud and Trust

It is important to keep in mind that while blockchain may offer better record keeping in a distributed way, this does not mean that it is complete trustless trust. There will still be major challenges for blockchain technology implementation in the years ahead. The biggest challenge of course will be to make sure that people understand how to use a blockchain and that they understand that even though a blockchain may make it tougher for fraudsters, it will not eradicate them from economic existence. It will just make them easier to find.

Although people are excited by digital currencies like Bitcoin, blockchain technology presents a much greater potential value for the economy than digital currencies. And that is because of its potential to reduce transactional friction in supply chains.

CHAPTER 8

QUANTUM COMPUTING

Another important technology for the future of supply chain is quantum computing. Quantum computing is a technology that uses qubits instead of bits in its computational data processing. Quantum data processing also uses parallel non-deterministic calculations, which allow for some very complicated problems to be solved much more rapidly than using standard bit-based computations.

Qubits are bits of data that exist in a quantum state — occupying positions at both 1 and 0 at the same time, in what is known as a *superposition*. These qubits are the processing power in a quantum computer, whereas bits that use only binary code of 1s and 0s power non-quantum computers.

Quantum physics is a scientific field of study developed in the 20th century that postulates that small particles can occupy two states of reality at the same time. This state is referred to as a quantum state. Its observation has been proven intractable because the process of measurement causes a collapse of the quantum state to one of two states of being in a binary structure.

There are a number of scientists and corporations working hard to bring the first commercially viable quantum computer to market. And while there are several kinds of quantum computers that are being developed, there would be two potential places for quantum computing to happen.

First, there is the potential for co-processors inside your personal computer to incorporate both quantum and traditional computational processing abilities. Second, the quantum computing processing power could be accessed in the cloud, where capacity to access a quantum computing server could be spun up or spun down, like with other kinds of cloud computing computational processing power.

The costs for a co-processor inside your standard computer have some important technological implications, and these costs would be borne by the computer owner. Conversely, quantum computing in the cloud could lever a use-based business model where you would essentially pay for QaaS (quantum as a service), like other SaaS (software as a service) models.

If you don't understand the intricate hardware workings of your computer's current processors, chances are that an upgrade to quantum will not be something that you personally need to perform. The same is true for coding. If you are not a software engineer, then managing the software transition to a co-processor interface that allows applications to toggle access between quantum processors and traditional processors is also not something you are likely to need to be able to do.

But quantum is likely to be something you benefit from. And it is likely something you need to be prepared for. And your life may be materially impacted by quantum computing and its increased processing power, which could foster scientific discovery, break blockchains, and trigger a global cybersecurity arms race. In supply chain predictive analytics and a push toward a real and complete AI, the impact could be exceptionally impactful.

But you may not notice a substantial change in the digital computer interfaces you use now because the adoption of quantum computing is likely to be an internally managed or cloud-based hardware upgrade, where a software interface is maintained to provide a normal UI/UX. Quantum computing is not a new internet. It is a new kind of computing. This means that it is more like a hardware change that may go unnoticed by the masses, despite its importance.

Quantum computing technology is not optional. The truth is, it is greatly needed. This is because computational powers are facing some potential limitations. In fact, many people working in technology will speak about a big near-term risk, and that's the limit of something called Moore's Law. Moore's Law, which is named after Intel founder Gordon Moore, is the notion that computational powers can be doubled while the costs are halved. This has made increasing computer processing power technology both more powerful and cheaper. And due to rising mountains of data created by e-commerce — and the needs for data in the supply chain — the need for quantum is rising.

Quantum has the potential to impact a wide range of industries in a general-purpose fashion — as has occurred with other kinds of computers that reached scalability and universal application. But just like classical computers, some industries will benefit more greatly from the leverage provided by more advanced computational power.

Supply chain and other industries already have strong use cases for predictive data analytics, machine learning, and artificial intelligence solutions. As such, it seems reasonable to conclude that quantum computing could take these efforts to the next level if and when quantum reaches commercialization. In other words, with quantum, real AI could become a much more attainable technology.

Figure 8-1: Quantum Computing Assessment by Sector

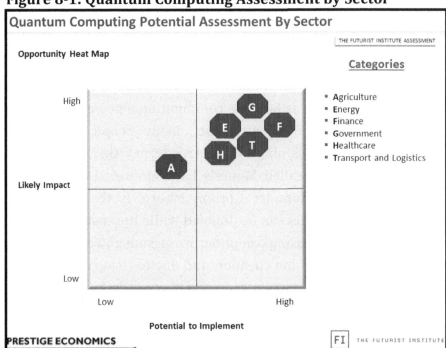

The Futurist Institute's Transport Quantum Assessment

Transport and logistics have tremendous use cases for quantum computing.

After all, these are fields with massive amounts of data — and a parabolically expanding data set. It is also an area where Big Data, predictive data analytics, machine learning, and AI are making big strides. And quantum computing could take supply chain data analysis to the next level.

The highest-value use cases for quantum computing would be tied to optimizing the resources that are used to move goods through the supply chain — as well as the actual vehicles in the process.

Figure 8-2: Quantum Computing Transport Assessment

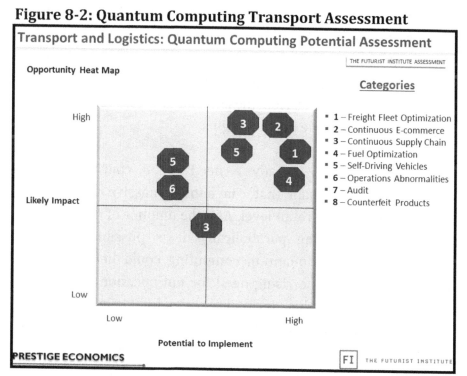

Transport and Logistics: Quantum Computing Potential Assessment

Opportunity Heat Map

THE FUTURIST INSTITUTE ASSESSMENT

Categories

- **1** – Freight Fleet Optimization
- **2** – Continuous E-commerce
- **3** – Continuous Supply Chain
- **4** – Fuel Optimization
- **5** – Self-Driving Vehicles
- **6** – Operations Abnormalities
- **7** – Audit
- **8** – Counterfeit Products

PRESTIGE ECONOMICS

FI THE FUTURIST INSTITUTE

The parts of transport and logistics with the highest implementation potential and the highest impact include freight fleet optimization, fuel optimization, continuous e-commerce, and the eventual creation of a comprehensive continuous supply chain that integrates retail, wholesale, distribution, and manufacturing parts of the supply chain in real time.

One of the educational games that places like MIT play with their supply chain executive education and graduate students is something called "the Beer Game." It is designed to highlight the problems and challenges of missing, incomplete, and uncommunicated data in a supply chain. The outcomes of this game are invariably the same; there are shortages and periods of oversupply that result in something called a bullwhip effect, in which a spike in demand at the end of the supply chain can take a long time to feed through to the origin of the goods. Worse yet, by the time the manufacturer sees the demand, it may already have fallen. This creates planning problems and bulges in the supply chain. In the real world, these kind of situations create inefficiencies and erode profit margins.

Right now, there is already a need for a continuous and responsive supply chain that can handle massive amounts of data, including at the retail level. And the amount of data related to this need is rising parabolically. It is possible that the processing power of quantum computing could help optimize this data and meet the rising need for optimization. Of course, early adopters of this technology would likely have big first-mover advantages and would need to be well capitalized to deploy early-stage commercialized quantum computing.

As with other kinds of technology discussed in this book, the companies that can make the required capital investments early and often will likely be the big winners. Those that fall behind are likely to suffer compounding lagging — and eventual failure.

Retail and wholesale margins are notoriously thin. And the edge will be found in maximum efficiency and logistics optimization. Quantum computing offers a theoretical use case here. This is also likely to be true for fuel optimization as well, which is likely to be a somewhat integrated risk and optimization issue with the fleetwide use of self-driving vehicles.

Aside from optimizing and pushing the U.S. supply chain to maximum efficiency, quantum computing use cases are likely to be similar to those in other fields, where quantum may have high value for identifying supply chain abnormalities and as an audit tool, as well as for identifying counterfeit goods within a system.

These use cases may not be the first points of implementation in logistics and transport, but they could bring significant value as supply chains seek total optimization and streamlining as well as identification and eradication of abnormalities that hurt margins.

In the coming decade, quantum computing is likely to reach commercialization — and it is likely to find one of its greatest use cases in real-time optimization of supply chains at scale. But the good news is, the interface you and I use may look just like the computer screens we see today.

Last Mile

Disruptions and Solutions

CHAPTER 9

CHALLENGES

Some of the biggest challenges of supply chains today are last mile issues. This term explicitly refers to delivering goods in the supply chain across the last mile of demand. And while this previously would have been to a retail store, the last mile today extends to people's homes.

In economies, like the United States, which have sprawling suburbs, the last mile is a logistical nightmare. And it is a source of significant additional costs. The technology to deliver goods is decades old, and it is dominated by mail truck, delivery truck, or other small vehicle. This will likely continue to be the majority of deliveries in the near term, because this is highly customized method of delivery.

But it is expensive.

And the rising the need to satisfy ever-increasing consumer demand for e-commerce goods is likely to prove almost never ending.

This makes last mile solutions one of the most critical areas for technological development in supply chain over the next decade. It is a priority, because it is a necessary requirement to continue to deliver goods in a rising-demand environment.

And it will be critical to controlling costs, so that e-commerce remains affordable. In short, solving last mile issues is a critical part of the equation to fulfill the promise of e-commerce.

While automated solutions have been deployed heavily in factories, warehouses, and distribution centers, this will not be the big challenge of supply chains for the next decade. As the self-service revolution accelerates, e-commerce demand will rise, and the greatest challenge for the supply chain of the next twenty years will be to ensure that people can get the goods they expect, quickly and cheaply.

E-commerce represented only 9.8 percent of total retail sales in Q3 2018. By 2030, it is likely to be double that level — around 20 percent of total retail sales or more. This means that innovative solutions will be required to get goods to people in the last mile of transport, unless we want to see the most prevalent job in the economy to be delivery person. This push to solve last mile issues is likely to be multi-faceted approach, and I expect the solution to last mile issues will require drones (on land and in the air), self-driving vehicles, 3D printing. and other solutions.

Companies need to have a strategy to ensure that they can effectively meet last mile needs of consumers. Because without solutions, the promises of e-commerce will be broken.

CHAPTER 10

SELF-DRIVING VEHICLES

For years, I have been writing that self-driving vehicles are coming. And today, in many ways, they are here. Or at least the beta testing is being done with increased visibility and scope out in the real world.

A number of companies have been working on self-driving vehicles, including Uber, Tesla, Apple, and GM; it is the Google spinoff, Waymo, that has taken the lead — by a wide margin. As of October 2018, Waymo had logged more than 10 million miles of vehicle driving, and it has continued to log 25,000 additional miles every day since.[1]

I rode in my first Waymo back in 2016, and I thought the vehicle seemed pretty market-ready then. Of course, back in 2016, Waymo had still logged less than 2 million miles.[2]

The point is that self-driving vehicles are coming. They've already been rolled out in a number of cities, and the rollout will continue. And it is likely to be gradual.

Part of the reason why the rollout of self-driving vehicles will be gradual is that the number of edge cases that limit the technological parameters of perfection is high. And in order to have self-driving vehicles engage in machine learning that eventually transitions into artificial intelligence, you need to expose the software to more data. In other words, you need the vehicles to drive more miles.

According to the U.S. Federal Highway Administration, Americans currently drive over 3.2 trillion miles per year, as you can see in Figure 10-1. So, the 10 million miles still is small in comparison. But as Waymo and other self-driving vehicles gain more exposure to miles driven, they will be deployed with accelerated frequency.

Figure 10-1: 12-Month Total Vehicle Miles Driven[3]

But Waymo isn't just testing cars. On my last trip to Silicon Valley, in the fall of 2018, Waymo-branded big rigs were driving around the facility, in the parking lots, and through the neighborhoods.

And this is where disruption in transportation can occur throughout the supply chain. While self-driving vehicles are likely to prove critical for delivery of goods in the last mile, they are also likely to be used for long-haul transport as well.

The big value proposition of self-driving vehicles is that they do not require drivers who need sleep, food, or other human necessities. As such, the constraints that have made freight more expensive in recent years, including limitations on hiring drivers who have been engendered by commercial drivers license — or CDL — regulations, will no longer apply.

Plus, last mile solutions could be solved, in part, by vehicles delivering retail goods without human involvement.

Self-driving vehicles will operate, in essence, as large on-road drones, if you will. They will not need a person to operate them, and they can autonomously make last mile deliveries without e-commerce succumbing to the limits of human abilities — or the actual number of humans who could be making deliveries.

Vehicles that are individually owned, or owned as part of a fleet that operates as a platform as a service, will eventually operate completely autonomously, without drivers using a mix of radar and lidar to determine their location and proximity to other people, animals, structures, and other vehicles. But the rollout will be gradual, with ever-increasing automation — and a reduced human presence.

For now, almost all self-driving vehicles have humans in place, just in case. Over the coming decade, those humans will vanish from driver seats and truck cabs.

Disruptive Impacts on Supply Chains

The disruptions to the supply chain of vehicle automation will be significant. It offers the ability to solve last mile issues and reduce the constraints of long-haul transport. Plus, industrial and consumer goods can be delivered more cheaply, more reliably, more safely, and more quickly without people.

But there will be a cost. And that will be a massive loss of transportation jobs in trucking, delivery, ridesharing, and other livery businesses. The U.S. Bureau of Labor Statistics expects that between 2.2 and 3.1 million jobs will be lost in coming years due to transportation vehicle automation.

Vehicle Automation in Practice

Here are few examples of some things you might see in supply chain with the broader adoption of vehicle automation:

- Industrial shipments arrive promptly and are offloaded automatically by self-driving vehicles that interface with your automated docking and loading stations.
- Retail consumer shipments are likely to be made by self-driving vehicles that are, in essence, full-size ground drones.
- Some vehicles may be set up as offices, reducing the need for short-haul flights and increasing productivity for workers when traveling.
- Commute times and traffic may be reduced, as traffic lights and stop signs may become irrelevant for vehicles that operate on location-based rules.
- Roving warehouses and distribution centers on wheels may be deployed to meet anticipatory demand of goods.

The big takeaway of this chapter is that self-driving vehicles are coming — despite any regulatory, technology, or edge-case challenges. And they will have a massive impact on the economy, the transportation industry, the nature of supply chain, and e-commerce.

The transition could be challenging as massive job losses in transportation occur and people on the road have accidents with autonomous vehicles on the road. This is part of the reason why the changes will be gradual.

But they will happen nonetheless.

CHAPTER 11

DRONES

One of the most important parts of last mile solutions to meet rising e-commerce demands in the United States (and globally) will be drones. These autonomous self-driving and self-flying vehicles are likely to use a mix of radar and lidar to get goods to people. Industrial drones will also be used for remote operations, to repair infrastructure, and to support business operations generally.

There aren't enough people to move all the goods through the supply chain. Nor can people work with the same speed and have the same strength as automated solutions like drones. This is why we expect retail and industrial drones to become important parts of receiving vendor supplies and sending goods to customers.

Retail consumer demand is often assumed to be the most critical use case for drones, but industrial drones may add the most economic value from an operational standpoint. Remote operations that require large equipment deliveries are more likely to be serviced by drones than someone's online order for toothpaste.

At the time this book went to print, most people thought of flying drones as toys with entertainment or kitsch value. You know, something you might buy at Brookstone as a holiday gift.

But for supply chain purposes, the greatest future kind of drone isn't going to be 12 inches wide and carry a digital camera around as it follows you to record every second of your next European vacation for posterity on Instagram and Snapchat.

Of course, those kinds of drones will grow in use as well. But those aren't the kinds of drones that will disrupt supply chains and work to solve last mile challenges. The better comparison for drones that will have big economic impact would be flying military drones that are adapted to have a dual use purpose for transporting industrial equipment to remote locations.

Oil and gas companies that operate in remote regions of the world will likely find high value in these kinds of flying industrial transport drones, which could fly-in pipes, drilling equipment, refinery parts, and other major equipment to remote areas, where roads are insufficient or nonexistent. The same is true for construction companies, manufacturers, and humanitarian organizations. Instead of building structures in impoverished, extremely remote areas, these could be transported by drones with wingspans of 5 or 10 meters — or even more.

Of course, we may also see flying drones used for e-commerce delivery. These could be used on their own or in conjunction with the on-road distribution center autonomous trucks.

Flying drones may also be used in warehouse and distribution facilities for picking and pulling. Through early 2019, most of the drones operating in warehouse and distribution centers were on wheels and operated in two-dimensional space.

But drones could go airborne in these facilities as e-commerce demands rise.

As for on-road drones, these could be deployed in an attempt to solve e-commerce last mile challenges until autonomous vehicles are on roads in force. After all, an autonomous van can carry a lot more goods than a small roving bot that looks like an in-office mail robot from the 1980s.

On-road delivery bots may be deployed in densely populated and relatively flat urban environments first. But they may be quickly surpassed by full-size autonomous delivery vehicles. And their biggest challenge will be the notion that "if man can make it, man can break it." And these bots may be subject to high levels of theft and mischief as they struggle to achieve broad adoption — especially in sprawling suburbs and areas with less-than-flat topographical layouts.

Disruptive Impacts on Supply Chains

Goods can be delivered more quickly and more cheaply. Plus, industrial and retail goods can be delivered more easily, more cheaply, and more effectively to remote locations that were almost impossible to reach. A big plus is that all of these delivery costs are likely to be significantly cheaper than current methods of transportation.

As with the other disruptive supply chain technologies ahead, there will be challenges for drones. One of the biggest risks will be that drones may be hackable and regulations may prohibit industrial and retail last mile drone development. This is especially a risk if roads and skies become very crowded with drones that appear to be everywhere.

In the end, the biggest supply chain value add for drones may not be in last mile solutions in the next 10 years. But it does seem likely that flying drones could have a material impact in extending the reach of global supply chains by increasing access to locations and markets that were previously exceptionally isolated.

CHAPTER 12

3D PRINTING

3D printing is the ability to print specific goods made out of materials that can be run though a machine. Although this was initially limited to some plastics, the next decade will bring a slew of advancements in the realm of 3D printing that will allow for increased use cases for printing metals and other materials, as well as entire buildings at scale.

The biggest potential change is that 3D printing could usher in an era of distributed manufacturing that disrupts the current manufacturing supply chain.

It is possible that some manufacturing will be replaced as people can effectively manufacture goods in their homes or in decentralized locations, using raw materials as inputs. Maintaining intellectual property rights will become critical as patented goods are printed and 3D printing presents the opportunity for a distributed supply chain with subscription-based access to intellectual property rights.

Disruptive Impacts on Supply Chains

The impact of a distributed network of 3D printers on logistics and supply chain in the United States and global economies cannot be stressed enough.

On the upside, more money can be made by owning the patents and intellectual property rights of goods. Plus, from a demand standpoint, the ability to print more items could increase demand. After all, consumer access would be instantaneous. And with distributed 3D printing facilities, it is imaginable that there would be reduced logistics costs and production costs due to shortened physical supply chains that reduce transportation, warehouse, distribution, and packaging requirements.

That's the rub for the supply chain: The need for logistics, transport, warehousing, distribution, and packaging would be greatly reduced in a 3D printing world.

There are also several other negative implications to establishing broad-based 3D printing.

The first is that printers stand to gain the widest margins rather than traditional manufacturers. This could have a negative impact on current manufacturing firms. Furthermore, there could be economic ripples if manufacturing jobs were to shift from concentrated facilities to distributed semi-retail outlets.

Another big change would be that physical commodity risks may shift to local or regional printers as printers own the materials rather than centralized and concentrated manufacturing facilities.

This means that 3D printers would need the ability and expertise to implement effective commodity risk management.

The significant risk management needs of 3D printers would also be paired with a need for 3D printing companies to have access to significant capital in order to make the massive capital investments required to disrupt the centralized nature of manufacturing and usher in an era of distributed manufacturing.

Due to these requirements, the companies that move into the 3D printing business would need to likely suffer significant financial losses before attaining profitability. And this description does not fit most traditional manufacturers, who have built their models on the value-add nature of manufacturing, where you buy input costs at a lower level than you sell the finished goods. This means that traditional manufacturers could be shut out of the 3D printing revolution.

After all, traditional manufacturers will likely continue to be required by their shareholders, investors, and owners to show profits and positive net income as well as cash flow. And only a technology company — either existing or to be created — would likely have investors willing to tolerate years or decades of losses in order to revolutionize and disrupt manufacturing.

Let's consider a recent and ongoing situation.

The death of department stores ensued when big tech companies pushed into e-commerce and retail became distributed and moved away from physical buildings to people's phones. Many retail chains suffered because they had to show profitability, while tech investors were willing to tolerate massive ongoing losses or low levels of profitability at companies like Amazon.

If tech companies were to come to 3D printing, it seems likely that their investors would again be willing to tolerate massive ongoing losses to disrupt traditional manufacturing. And traditional manufacturing firms would likely be at a significant disadvantage as they would be required to show profits — and not ongoing losses.

The massive upfront capital requirements of a distributed network of 3D printers and the willingness of investors to tolerate significant ongoing losses, means that major incumbent technology firms would have the greatest potential to advance this business model.

The impact on the economy of a transition to distributed 3D printing manufacturing cannot be understated.

3D Printing in Practice

Here are few examples of some things you might see with the adoption of distributed 3D printing manufacturing:

- Distributed networks of print shops produces consumer and household goods.
- Industrial network of print shops — or print shops housed in factories — prints licensed materials on-site on demand and does not need to order them to be shipped.
- Printing manufactured goods becomes a license and subscription model with limited and unlimited print runs for goods to be manufactured. You license parts you will need for future manufactured goods.
- Value is created by owning the intellectual property of industrial design rather than by owning the means of production.
- When you need a bigger house, you just tear down the current house, and a new home is printed overnight.
- Regional printers own plastics and metals warehouses to print a wide range of consumer and industrial goods on demand.

As you can see, the shift could be massive. But it is unlikely to happen instantaneously. And manufacturers may try to distribute some of their manufacturing. But over the next decade, we are likely to see more 3D printing — and the beginning of distributed manufacturing and a disruption to traditional manufacturing supply chains.

Economic Risks

CHAPTER 13

ENTITLEMENTS

The U.S. national debt was above $22 trillion at the beginning of 2019. That's a lot. And it is likely to rise significantly over the next 10 years. In fact, the U.S. national debt could eclipse $40 trillion by 2030. This will likely require significantly higher tax rates to finance ballooning U.S. debt obligations — even if interest rates remain relatively low. This is why higher debt levels would lower long-term potential U.S. GDP growth.

But the biggest long-term risk to the U.S. economy isn't the debt alone. On top of the current $22 trillion in national debt are entitlement obligations. These Social Security, Medicare, and Medicaid obligations currently represent $200 trillion in off-balance sheet unfunded government liabilities.

And the U.S. government budget, as a recent percentage of GDP, may only be able to bear entitlements and the interest on U.S. debt until 2030, which is why we see the national debt and tax rates rising significantly in the future.

Entitlements

U.S. entitlements, including Medicare, Medicaid, and Social Security, are financed by payroll taxes from workers. Payroll taxes are separate from income taxes, and while income tax rates could fall if fiscal policies change, payroll taxes are on a one-way trip higher. You see, entitlements are wildly underfunded.

All the sovereign debt in the world totals around $60 trillion.[1] That is the debt cumulatively held by all national governments in the world. But the size of unfunded U.S. entitlements might be more than three times that level. That's right: The unfunded, off-balance sheet obligations for Medicare, Medicaid, and Social Security could be $200 trillion.[2]

This level of off-balance sheet debt obligation existentially threatens the U.S. economy. The Heritage Foundation has taken calculations from the U.S. Congressional Budget Office about entitlements to create Figure 13-1, which looks quite catastrophic. Basically, by 2030, all U.S. tax revenue will be consumed by entitlements and the interest on the national debt. And these were the dismal calculations before tax reform and the most recent U.S. budget threatened to increase the national debt further.

The year 2030 is not that far in the future, and the clock is ticking. But despite the magnitude of the entitlements problem, this issue was not seriously addressed during or following the 2018 midterm elections. Don't expect it to be addressed in the 2020 election cycle either.

Figure 13-1: Tax Revenue Spent on Entitlements[3]

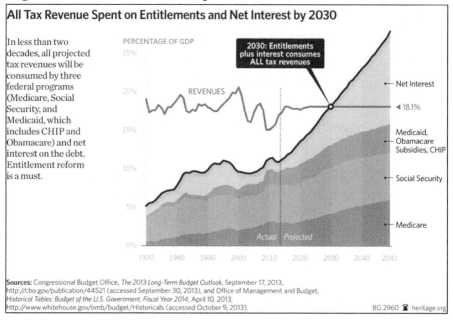

All Tax Revenue Spent on Entitlements and Net Interest by 2030

In less than two decades, all projected tax revenues will be consumed by three federal programs (Medicare, Social Security, and Medicaid, which includes CHIP and Obamacare) and net interest on the debt. Entitlement reform is a must.

PERCENTAGE OF GDP

2030: Entitlements plus interest consumes ALL tax revenues

REVENUES

Net Interest

18.1%

Medicaid, Obamacare Subsidies, CHIP

Social Security

Medicare

Actual | Projected

Sources: Congressional Budget Office, *The 2013 Long-Term Budget Outlook*, September 17, 2013, http://cbo.gov/publication/44521 (accessed September 30, 2013), and Office of Management and Budget, *Historical Tables: Budget of the U.S. Government, Fiscal Year 2014*, April 10, 2013, http://www.whitehouse.gov/omb/budget/Historicals (accessed October 9, 2013).

BG 2960 ☎ heritage.org

The Grandfather of U.S. Social Security

Part of the problem with entitlements stems from their origins. The U.S. Social Security Administration website credits Otto von Bismarck as the grandfather of U.S. entitlements. Bismarck's portrait is even on the U.S. Social Security Administration's website (Figure 13-2).

Bismarck was a powerful politician known for his use of *Realpolitik*, a political doctrine built on pragmatism to advance national self-interests. For him, entitlements were convenient and expedient. Unfortunately, that is no longer the case. Today, entitlements threaten to crush the U.S. economy with increased levels of debt. And without reform, they could decimate the U.S. workforce.

Bismarck's system was also sustainable. His system guaranteed a pension to German workers over 70, but the average life expectancy in Germany in the late 1880s was only 40.[4] In other words, so few people were expected to receive the benefits that the program's cost would be negligible.

Bismarck rigged entitlements to help crush his political opponents, without having to pay out. But the current entitlement system in the United States is an unfunded liability that threatens to crush the entire economy and usher in a labor market *robocalypse.* Plus, fixing entitlements presents a horrible dilemma as many Americans rely heavily on entitlements for income (Figure 13-3).

Figure 13-2: Grandfather of Social Security, Otto von Bismarck[5]

But how did this system break down?

Bismarck had such a good thing going. What happened?

This can be answered in one word: demographics. But before we dive into that topic, let's consider the disruptive likely impact of entitlements on supply chains. Most importantly, it presents a risk of increased corporate taxes, sales taxes, and payroll taxes.

The national debt could very well double in the next 10 years, presenting massive risks to potential economic growth — and posing risks to profitability in all parts of the U.S. economy and the U.S. supply chain.

Figure 13-3: Expected Importance of Social Security[6]

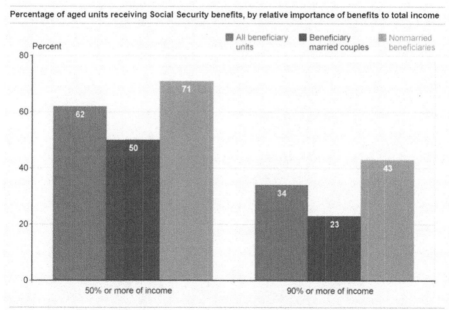

Percentage of aged units receiving Social Security benefits, by relative importance of benefits to total income

SOURCE: SSA calculations from the March 2016 Annual Social and Economic Supplement to the Current Population Survey.

NOTE: An aged unit is a married couple living together or a nonmarried person, which also includes persons who are separated or married but not living together.

CHAPTER 14

DEMOGRAPHICS

U.S. population growth has slowed sharply, and this demographic shift appears unstoppable. Plus, as birthrates have fallen, life expectancy has also risen. This compounds the funding shortfalls for entitlements.

Population growth in the United States has fallen from annual rates of over 1.5 percent per year during the 1950s and early 1960s to just 0.7 percent since 2011.[1] Some of this slowing in population growth is due to a decline in the U.S. fertility rate. In general, fertility rates have been dropping globally, but according to demographer Jonathan Last, the U.S. fertility rate is still relatively high at 1.93.[2]

However, even though the U.S. total fertility rate is relatively high compared to other industrialized nations, it is below the 2.1 percent "golden number," which is required to maintain a population, according to Last.[3]

This is a huge problem for maintaining entitlements. After all, the entitlement system worked really well in 1940, when there were 159.4 workers per beneficiary (Figure 14-1), but it is more challenging since that number fell to only 2.8 in 2013. Plus, it is likely to fall to two workers per beneficiary by 2040.[4]

Entitlements are under siege from both sides: The birth rate has fallen — and life expectancy has risen.

Figure 14-1: Ratio of Workers to Social Security Beneficiaries[5]

Year	Covered Workers (in thousands)	Beneficiaries (in thousands)	Ratio
1940	35,390	222	159.4
1945	46,390	1,106	41.9
1950	48,280	2,930	16.5
1955	65,200	7,563	8.6
1960	72,530	14,262	5.1
1965	80,680	20,157	4.0
1970	93,090	25,186	3.7
1975	100,200	31,123	3.2
1980	113,656	35,118	3.2
1985	120,565	36,650	3.3
1990	133,672	39,470	3.4
1995	141,446	43,107	3.3
2000	155,295	45,166	3.4
2005	159,081	48,133	3.3
2010	156,725	53,398	2.9
2013	163,221	57,471	2.8

In addition to lower birth rates, U.S. life expectancy has doubled since Bismarck implemented entitlements in Germany in 1889 — from around 40 years to above 80 years. Plus, the age at which people receive entitlements benefits has actually been lowered from 70 to 65. On top of a significantly larger population being eligible to receive entitlements, the medical costs required to support an aging population have also risen.

Everything might be OK — if U.S. population growth was extremely robust. But it is not. Plus, the current administration is pushing hard to reduce illegal immigration to the United States. While this can have some benefits for society and the economy in some ways, it can also reduce the pace of population growth and lower the average U.S. birthrate.

Population growth has slowed to less than half the rate seen during the baby boom years, and the total U.S. fertility rate is below the "golden number" that is required to maintain a population. As Last notes, "Social Security is, in essence, a Ponzi scheme. Like all Ponzi schemes, it works just fine — so long as the intake of new participants continues to increase."[6] Unfortunately, entitlements are nearing a breaking point.

A big problem with slowing birthrates is the manifestation of a shrinking tax base at the same time that unfunded financial obligations are rising. This means that the unfunded $200 trillion or more in future entitlements payments will be borne by an increasingly smaller proportion of the population. And as the population ages, there is another issue: Who will do the work?

Payroll Taxes and a Shrinking U.S. Tax Base

When there is a tax shortfall, there is often a need to raise taxes. And there are risks of significantly higher payroll taxes in the not-too-distant future. Slowing population growth is likely to exacerbate U.S. debt and entitlement burdens by accelerating the reduction in the U.S. tax base — especially for payroll taxes, which fund entitlements. And if entitlements obligations cannot be met with current funding, payroll taxes will rise.

So, who pays payroll taxes?

Employees split entitlement costs with their employers, who pay half. This means that if entitlement costs rise, the cost for an employer to keep a person employed will also increase. The substitution effect of automation for labor would then likely accelerate because of the financial incentives in place for employers.

As payroll taxes increase to cover the costs associated with underfunded entitlements, the financial incentives for employers to shift work away from human laborers and add technology are likely to be reinforced. A number of my clients have shared their concerns about the risk of rising costs associated with health care costs for their workers.

How do you think employers will feel about the burden of paying much higher payroll taxes? They do pay half of them, after all.

Entrepreneurs at Risk

Rising entitlement costs and payroll taxes could also stifle entrepreneurship. Unlike employees, who split payroll tax obligations with their employers, self-employed people bear the full brunt of payroll taxes personally. The rate is currently 15.3 percent of income.[7] In the future, that rate will rise faster for entrepreneurs since they will not be splitting the increase in payroll taxes with an employer. If entitlements are not drastically overhauled, a self-employment tax rate of 25 percent by 2030 is not inconceivable.

Increasingly high self-employment tax rates are likely to stifle entrepreneurship and hurt self-employed workers. According to an article by the Pew Foundation, the percent of workers who are self-employed fell from 11.4 percent in 1990 to 10 percent in 2014.[8] More importantly, the Pew Foundation notes that 30 percent of U.S. jobs are held "by the self-employed and the workers they hire."[9] In other words, in 2014, 14.6 million self-employed workers hired another 29.4 million workers, making 30 percent of employees.

With the prospect of entitlement shortfalls and a shrinking tax base, self-employment tax rates are going to rise. The impact of these additional costs is likely to engender a continued downward trend in the percent of self-employed workers. Plus, workers in the so-called gig economy — like all 1099s — are also subject to self-employment taxes. This could also make the existence of the gig economy less tenable as payroll taxes rise.

Declines in birth rates, increased longevity, rising health care costs, falling labor force participation rates, and overincentivized automation are likely to accelerate and exacerbate the problems of the U.S. national defined benefits programs known as entitlements — programs that worked best financially when the age at which one received benefits exceeded life expectancy by 30 years.

One would think that this topic would be at the forefront of political discourse, but it is not.

As I noted in my book *Midterm Economics*, the entitlements system was ignored during the 2017 tax reform act, and I also expected it would be ignored in the 2018 midterms, which it was. Furthermore, I expect this topic will likely remain ignored until and after the 2020 presidential election. In fact, this topic is likely to go largely unaddressed until it is too late.

The reason is that politicians that want to be reelected won't touch this existential economic threat with a 10-foot pole.

Global Risks of Slowing Population Growth

Unfortunately, the slowing population growth and the rising burden of entitlements is not just something occurring in the United States. It is also happening in countries all over the world. These dynamics will change consumer behavior as we find the population shifts older and overall population growth slows This will have significant and important implications for the global economy — and the future of supply chain.

Supply Chain Implications

It's tough to get strong GDP growth with slowing or falling population growth. This will be a major challenge for economies, like the United States, that are driven by goods consumption.

Additionally, even as the rise of off-balance sheet debt obligations rises in the face of unquestionable demographic realities, the talk of universal basic income — or UBI — is likely to increase.

UBI is the notion that governments will give a set amount of money to every one of its citizens without requiring them to do any work. And while everyone loves the sound of free money, there is no such thing. In fact, UBI would only make the debt situation worse, by increasing the financial obligations of governments that are already burdened by demographic trends that have upended their entitlement systems, which includes both increased longevity and decreased birth rates.

But people like free stuff, so the push for UBI will increase significantly in the next 10 years, to the point where political systems that look like communism may emerge.

The changes in demographics, entitlements, and taxation ahead could undermine the entire capitalist economic system, which would have massively negative consequences for businesses, including transportation and supply chain. The same, although to an even greater degree, would be true of the disruptive reemergence of communist economies. This could greatly impact global supply chains, the cost of trade, and profitability as well as present going concern issues in certain neo-communist regions.

Market Risks and Opportunities

CHAPTER 15

FINANCIALIZATION OF MARKETS

One critical factor that will become increasingly important for supply chain and businesses will be the financialization of markets. In recent years, financial markets have begun to move more in sync with one another. This presents risks that financial market volatility could be compounded across markets, which see high levels of multicollinearity.

As financial markets move more closely together, there is also a greater risk of equity market and other financial market volatility due to increased automation of trading. A broad proliferation of algorithm — algo — traders has been advancing at breakneck pace at institutional investment firms and hedge funds for over a decade.

But algo trading has increasingly been democratized so that retail investors are now exposed. Roboadvisors exacerbate the potential for retail investors to be swept away in Newtonian moves of technical trading, where swings high are hard and fast surges, while declines become collapses.

This means that markets across the board — the dollar, oil, gold, foreign exchange, metals, and equity markets — will respond with more significant swings on fundamental changes in data that challenge the direction of technical trades, which reflect a piling of automated sentiment. This is a subject I discuss at length in my book *Jobs for Robots*.

For supply chain, these advancing dynamics mean that financial risk management will become more complicated as commodity, currency, and interest rate risks move more closely together, requiring deeper analytics and financial market understanding to effectively identify and manage risks.

One important dynamic that has been emerging, even as this book was going to print, is the development of an on-road U.S. freight futures market. The group Freightwaves has been pushing this development with an upcoming launch of its trading platform and futures market at the end of March 2019. I expect these solutions will find traction, and I expect more risk management solutions will be created for freight in the future.

The challenge will be to get companies in the supply chain to embrace risk management. It is a major change of financial operation, but that often takes a while for a full-blown culture of risk to spread in an industry — or even in a single company.

But over the next 10 years, I expect increased risk management adoption in supply chain and freight industries — especially as correlated risks make being unhedged — or "going naked" as traders call it — particularly unpleasant.

CHAPTER 16

DIGITAL CURRENCIES

Bitcoin and blockchain are two topics that often get conflated. In Chapter 7, I discussed blockchain technology. which can be used to reduce transactional friction in the supply chain, as well as many other high value-add economic activities.

But while the supply chain use cases of blockchain are likely to be the most valuable for the economy, in terms of economic impact, the most famous use of blockchain is as the technology that supports digital currencies like Bitcoin.

The reason digital currencies have been so hotly watched is because of the massive amounts of wealth that were created essentially out of nowhere. Let's discuss some basics you need to know.

First off, digital currencies are virtual and not physical. As such, digital currencies are token currencies that are not backed by reserves, not controlled by central banks, and not physically printed. The current versions of digital currencies may turn out to be just the beta versions of the eventual winners in this space.

Digital currencies are maintained in virtual accounts. They are designed to be mediums of exchange. But some people have been buying, holding, and trading them as a store of value. The leading current digital currencies include Bitcoin and Ethereum, but new and different additional digital currencies are likely to be created over the next decade.

A key metric that will determine future use and adoption of digital currencies will be transactions per second. And for now, the effectiveness of digital currencies, in terms of transactions per second, is not great.

In Figure 16-1, I have shown the different transactions per second across a number of different payment processors.

Figure 16-1: Transactions per Second[1]

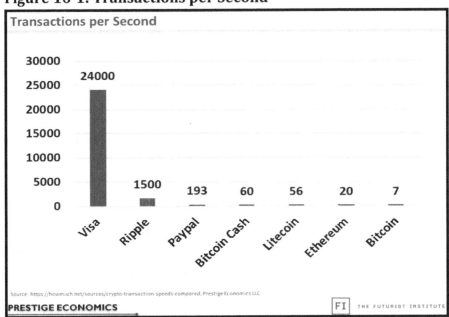

As you can see, the credit card company Visa absolutely crushes the competition at 24,000 transactions per second. Meanwhile, Ripple is the cryptocurrency with the highest transactions per second at a much lower — but respectable — 1,500 per second. However, the beloved cryptocurrency Ethereum is at only 20 transactions per second.

And the headline-grabber Bitcoin is way down the line at only seven transactions per second. That's very low by comparison. And it means that Bitcoin is unlikely to become a digital currency with long-lived staying power for high-frequency international transactions, like those that occur every second in the supply chain. This means that even though companies need to be increasingly ready to make and receive payments in digital currencies over the next decade, it may take longer than many people think for digital payments to become a major share of global payments. And even then, some of the best-known anonymous cryptos like Bitcoin and Ethereum may be left out in the cold because their use is impractical from a transaction per second standpoint.

Digital currencies initially offered the potential for companies to better manage their foreign exchange risks, but the volatility of digital currencies like Bitcoin is much higher than the volatility of physical currencies. And with the exception of Ripple, many digital currencies continue to operate outside of the international SWIFT banking regulations. The winner of the digital currency race may be traditional payment incumbents like Visa. And if a cryptocurrency hopes to be used broadly, it needs a solid level of transactions per second, which may take time to establish.

Political Risks and Disruptions

CHAPTER 17

NATIONALISM AND REGIONALISM

The global political climate has changed in the past few years. Nationalism, which prioritizes the nation above the global community, has represented a surprising turn in political sentiment that pushes against the post-World War Two trend toward globalization and supranational cooperation. In particular, the nationalist turn in U.S. and U.K. politics has made it clear that nationalist politics could become more prevalent.

One could argue that some of the rise in nationalism has been engendered by a lack of rising real incomes. But some of it was certainly due to the manipulation of social media by bad actors to exploit differences within populaces to sow seeds of divisiveness.

This exploitation of social media as de facto digital IEDs is likely to continue and accelerate as long as social media firms remain focused purely on their bottom line and operate in a bubble with little ethical oversight ingrained into their platforms. It may take regulation to enact this level of change, and the Europeans have been trying to push back. But it is an uphill battle.

Without changes in the way social media is used, consumed, and manipulated with fake news, the waves of nationalism and political divisiveness are going to make ever-greater waves against a previously stable sea of globalization.

Accompanying a rising trend of nationalism, we are also likely to see a rise of regionalist movements in coming years. From a geographic standpoint, countries could split apart due to regional movements to form new countries as political discontent rises.

In a world of increased discontent driven by political polarization, borders of western countries are at risk of being peacefully redrawn — by plebiscite, election, or referendum. Particularly at risk are countries currently in the post-Brexit United Kingdom as well as regions in Spain that have agitated for political independence for hundreds of years. Even in the United States, the discussion will increase around the secession movement in Texas, but the odds are likely to remain exceptionally low.

Although much of the push of nationalism against globalization as well as the push of regionalism against nationalism may prove to be more rhetoric than action. But in some places these dynamics could become more actionable movements — especially if political polarization engenders an increase in voter dissatisfaction. An economic downturn could significantly exacerbate the appeal of nationalist and regionalist rhetoric in a high number of countries. After all, the recent rise of nationalist and regionalist sentiments has occurred despite a relatively solid global economy. What happens if the economy falters?

Disruptive Impacts on Supply Chains

For supply chain professionals, there are clear implications. Companies may need to respond to nationalist changes in trade regulations that could include increased tariffs, stricter border controls, and an all-out global trade war.

Nationalist and Regionalist Risks in Practice

Here are few examples of some things you might see over the next 10 years:

- More banking and finance jobs move in large numbers from London to European Union cities, especially Frankfurt.
- Scotland emerges as an independent country, with its currency status temporarily in flux and its trade policies entirely rewritten.
- Ireland potentially unites with Ulster to form a greater Ireland in the European Union.
- Catalonia and Basqueland agitate as independent counties, with a further devolved federalist Spanish system.
- Despite European regionalism, new countries that splinter from European Union and/or the European Monetary Union may seek to remain in the broader supranational organization.
- California and Texas secession movements gain more followers and more press, but they remain extremely unlikely.

Takeaways

Supply chain professionals and companies with global supply chains will need to respond to changes that accompany nationalist tendencies, regional devolution, and even successful regionalist movements.

On a practical level, these changes could include political uncertainty, cash flows in and out of affected countries, labor market dynamics in other regions, and changes in trade policy and long-established regulations. Risks to changes in supply chain end-market demand or upstream vendor access may need to be considered. And one of the biggest areas where things could change if borders are redrawn is trade.

CHAPTER 18

TRADE

Nationalist politics present risks of isolationist trade policies, which could significantly impact supply chains globally. We have already started to see these dynamics as an extension of recent nationalist sentiment, especially in the United States.

Additional trade restrictions to protect national interests above international interests are a major risk across the global economy and are likely to emerge from the United States and other economies.

These kinds of trade risks became a major red flag for the International Monetary Fund in 2018, due in large part because very strong global growth in 2017 was attributed to strong global trade. If trade conflicts continue and proliferate further, the downside risks to economic growth will increase.

To put these risks in perspective, trade risks were on no one's radar as a major risk of any kind in 2015. Very few analysts considered them to be credible risks well into 2018, even after U.S. Section 232 and 301 tariffs were announced.

From a supply chain standpoint, this means that global economic growth is at risk of destabilization and recession due to trade risks. And if the global economy slows, this would erode freight demand and profits.

At the time this book went to print, the economic expansion since the Great Recession of 2007-2009 was one of the longest in history, with some economists forecasting that it would turn into the longest expansion in history. But trade wars could dampen the outlook significantly.

As Ben Bernanke noted on 4 January 2019 at a panel with Fed Chair Powell and fellow Fed Chair Yellen, business cycles don't die of old age; they get murdered. In other words, economic expansions usually end because of something overlooked that creates a shock to the economic system.

In the host of usual suspects, very high valuations of tech equities and elevated trade war risks top the list. For supply chain professionals, trade risks are likely to remain front and center. And they are unlikely to be easily resolved, especially if economic growth slows. This makes trade a risk that could be on the docket of disruptive risks for the coming decade.

CHAPTER 19

PRIVACY

Another policy risk and challenge of the next decade will be privacy. IoT will put "smart" devices in our homes and offices, while drones and last mile solutions will be abundant in our immediate physical proximity.

The digital and automated swarm may be — and is in fact already being — met with resistance.

And the amazing technological innovations that could make supply chain operate more effectively, more rapidly, and more efficiently will likely have strings attached. Companies may be required to make drone and automated vehicle actions more transparent, while also taking steps to ensure data privacy.

European pushback on data has already begun with GDPR and privacy prioritization. But this is just the start of the war over data and the preservation of privacy. And it is likely to be a protracted battle that lasts throughout the coming decade, until technology is either pushed back or, more likely, people forget what real privacy is like.

Disruptive Impacts on Supply Chains

Companies will be required to share more about their company activities, and companies will be required to protect their client data more vigorously. This means that greater supply chain transparency may be required as well. One way this could be pushed forward would be with the use of blockchain, as both a source of more comprehensive corporate activity records and as a means of advanced encryption.

Privacy in Practice

Some of the changes of privacy in practice could include more limitations placed on protecting and sharing client data as well as limitations on monitoring, watching, and listening to people. As a more tangible example, drones could be required to be registered and identifiable by cellphones pointed at them.

Privacy is something that we have blissfully enjoyed and taken for granted historically. And it may be gone in the next decade. In effect, there may be no way to go back to complete privacy from an IoT world. But having all of your data "out there" presents risks for corporations as well as individuals.

And this is tied to the next big disruptive risk: security.

CHAPTER 20

SECURITY

Increased security will be critical in the next decade — especially in supply chains.

On the one hand, there is a need for greater levels of cybersecurity to protect data, business operations, trade secrets, and financial accounts. But there is also a rising need for security in supply chain operations as counterfeiting improves over the coming decade.

With a world of IoT devices, cybersecurity risks increase exponentially as the volume of data also increases parabolically. With more FinTech use, the risks of exchange and financial account hacking increase. Even Bitcoin and other digital currency wallets have been subject to frequent hacking.

Ransomware has also increased significantly in recent years, where payments are required to use or access a device or website. And these risks and challenges are only going to become increasing problems.

With everything online, every *thing* becomes hackable: refrigerators, self-driving cars, bank accounts, etc. There is no upside for security risks.

All of the wonderful autonomous vehicles, the self-driving on-road distribution centers, the industrial flying drones, and the urban on-road delivery drones can be hacked. This means that while supply chain will have tremendous innovations at its disposal to increase the speed of delivery, the efficiency of operations, and the access of its asset, the technological marvels that present tremendous opportunity also present great threats.

Disruptive Impacts on Supply Chains
There are a number of disruptive impacts that security issues could pose to supply chain. You could find supplies disrupted by transportation hijacking, hacking, and held for cyber ransom.

Alternatively, on-site machinery, flying warehouse drones, or even entire fleets of autonomous trucks could be hacked and held for cyber ransom. And of course customer data could be stolen, and financial accounts could be hacked.

Many publicly traded companies already carry cybersecurity insurance and have cybersecurity experts on their boards. This is one of the reasons that the National Association of Corporate Directors partnered with Carnegie Mellon University to create a cybersecurity training certification. It's a program I completed in 2018, and it's only going to gain more traction as cybersecurity issues threaten to become going concern issues. And supply chain companies are particularly at risk from this kind of threat.

Of course, there are different kinds of security threats. On the one hand, there are cybersecurity threats. On the other hand, there are counterfeiting risks.

Cybersecurity risks are more likely to be detected, either by software or because of a ransomware demand. But the other big security risk — posed by counterfeiting technology — is intentionally difficult to identify. And over the next decade, counterfeit goods are likely to become increasingly more difficult to detect.

The most vulnerable goods to this kind of risk are military goods, dual use technology goods, and high-value consumer tech goods. For this reason, there are national security risks at play from this kind of challenge as well as financial and business risks.

One company, Securemarking, has been working to mark goods to prevent counterfeiting by using invisible markings to mark genuine goods. But other technologies are likely to be deployed over the next 10 years to ensure the integrity of the supply chain, including blockchain as a more comprehensive and permanent record as well as other new kinds of physical marking and virtual technologies.

Marking goods is a way to prevent counterfeiting and to protect intellectual property. Although this adoption is likely to be most commonly used initially for goods of high technological, high intellectual property, or military value. Marking goods becomes increasingly important as we transition to an intellectual capital economy.

There are a number of value-adds from securely marking goods at the beginning of the supply chain and testing them throughout — and at the end of — the supply chain. These value-adds include that the vendor of goods can be verified, the intermediary location of goods can be verified, and the end customers can verify that they have received genuine goods. Even simply deploying this technology may reduce counterfeiting and hijacking of goods shipments — especially if markings are a critical part of verifying authenticity of end consumers.

In practical terms, nanotechnology markings, which are invisible to the naked eye, could be placed on inverted delta airplane parts and verified by the customer. Blockchain technology could also be integrated with the marking technology to verify the supply chain parties involved in every physical transaction of the goods throughout their chain of custody. As with other blockchain technology use cases, the integrated use of securely marking goods and blockchain will be most valuable for protecting individual consumers as well as for providing greater transparency for high-value supply chain goods.

The priority list for increased diligent supply chain controls over the next decade will be agricultural goods, pharmaceuticals, inverted delta parts, military goods, dual use technology goods, and consumer tech goods. Unfortunately, marking goods and using blockchain will not mitigate or solve all supply chain risks. After all, those massive industrial drones could be increasingly used for hijacking with little risk to the individuals involved. Furthermore, these technologies will not protect the intellectual capital value chain.

Better Mousetrap, Better Mouse

While marking goods will help secure traditional supply chains, elevated levels of cybersecurity will be required if 3D printing ushers in an era of distributed manufacturing, in which the value is in the digital printing instructions rather than in the actual physical goods created.

And while quantum computing presents extremely high value use cases for data analysis, some of its greatest value uses of the next decade will be in decrypting non-quantum encryptions as well as creating new quantum encryptions.

Even the lauded encryptions of blockchains and digital currencies will be at risk. In fact, there is a debate raging among quantum computing theorists as to how big the impact of quantum computing could be. Some argue that blockchains and cryptocurrencies will be safe. Still others propose creating quantum blockchains when this becomes an issue. Since the technology does not yet exist, it is difficult to take a firm stand on this, but cybersecurity risks are unlikely to go down if computer decryption and processing power increase exponentially. This is a topic I explored in depth in my book *Quantum: Computing Nouveau.*

For supply chain professionals, the big takeaway is that supply chains will be more vulnerable to cyberattacks, counterfeiting, and hijacking than ever before. Even though blockchain may be viewed from a cybersecurity standpoint as a better mousetrap, quantum is likely to be a better mouse. Nothing will be safe.

Staying Futureproof

CHAPTER 21

INCORPORATING FUTURIST STRATEGIES

The most important thing that a supply chain professional can do when facing an unprecedented era of disruption is to consider new and emerging technologies for their value-add uses in the supply chain as well as for the potential threats they could pose to a supply chain business.

As I mentioned in a previous chapter, the notion to consider here is that *if man can make it, he can break it.* This represents the two sides of each technology coin: the upside opportunity and the downside risk. An example of this idea is how industrial drones that may transport pipelines to remote oil pads can also be used to hijack shipments of exotic fruits, auto parts, or cobalt.

Although it is important to incorporate new and emerging technology risks and opportunities into your strategic planning, perhaps the most important thing when considering futurist strategies is not to get caught up in the hype of technologies that are just barely past the ideation.

Some technologies are headline grabbers, but they are not quite at MVP — or minimum viable product. For these kinds of innovations, it's not worth spending too much time on them. I mean, you have to be careful about worrying about technology that does not exist yet — or have any potential to come to fruition.

A lot can happen in 10 years for technology.

After all, Bitcoin turned 10 years old in the month before the publication of this book. Similarly, Blackberry was at its most dominant market position 10 years before this book was released.

But even though technology can change rapidly, it is also important not to get too focused on technological expectations 50 years in the future. A strategic plan that is overly focused on technology that won't be commercialized for decades, like mining asteroids, is just as bad as a strategic plan that ignores technology that is going through rigorous beta testing and initial rollouts, like autonomous vehicles.

There is a careful balance to walk between being a trusted innovation thought partner and being a *Star Trek* fanboy. Make sure that your focus is on ROI, commercialization potential, and medium-term disruptive innovation potential.

Leave colonizing Mars and Saturn's moon Titan to sci-fi script doctors in Hollywood, fans at Comic-Con, and Elon Musk.

CHAPTER 22

BUILDING A CORPORATE FUTURIST PRACTICE

Being a futurist doesn't need to be a solo activity. In fact, an important question I have been asked with greater frequency in recent months is how to build a futurist practice within a corporate entity. There are several critical value-adds of this kind of initiative.

There are four key requirements for building a successful futurist practice:

- **Senior Leadership Support**
- **Demonstrating Thought Leadership**
- **Internal Strategic Support**
- **External Relationship Building**

As with all internal corporate initiatives, the most important part is to have senior leadership support or buy in for a futurist initiative. As I've alluded to in this book and in other books I've written, as well as in the courses by The Futurist Institute, there are several big value-adds to being a futurist. Most importantly, you can stay ahead of trends that present either threats or opportunities to your business — or your personal career.

Obviously, when trying to **get support from senior leadership** to build a futurist practice, the most important thing you can do is underscore the value it would bring to the business from the strategic vantage point of both identifying upside opportunities and mitigating downside risks for your corporate entity.

Once you have buy in, the practice needs to **demonstrate thought leadership** — and more importantly, thought partnership. One way to do this is to focus on generating multipurpose content. This could include content that could be used for **internal strategic planning** as well as by your sales team for **external relationship building** that puts your company in the enviable position of a thought partner.

There is a clear and growing need to remain strategically on top of material new and emerging market technologies. This does not mean that you need to have a strategy for all of them. After all, most technological innovations fail. But some that have multibillion-dollar investor backing have been identified as critical dual use technologies (with military and civilian use cases), and technologies in the early stages of commercialization need to be prioritized.

Providing consistent high-value internal support and enhancing external corporate visibility is the best way to build up a futurist practice — and to support your own career progression as a futurist. This concept of building a futurist practice is a core subject I discuss in my forthcoming book *Spikes: Growth Hacking Leadership*.

CHAPTER 23

INDIVIDUAL STRATEGIES TO BE FUTUREPROOF

Becoming a futurist and building a futurist practice in your corporation are just a couple ways to make yourself futureproof. After all, if you are on the cutting edge, and you help keep others there, it makes you invaluable.

It reminds me of the joke about two economists being attacked by a bear. One economist stops to put on his running shoes. And the other economist says, "What are you doing? You'll never be able to outrun the bear!" The economist with the running shoes replies, "I don't need to be able to outrun the bear — I just need to be able to outrun you."

If technology is nipping at the heels of supply chain and transportation jobs, make sure you are at the vanguard of change. This is an extension of the concept of perpetual learning that I proposed in my books *Jobs for Robots* and *Robot-Proof Yourself*. Essentially, if you want to be futureproof, you have to be the first to embrace the future. And you have to help others see you as a leader keeping the company at the head of the pack.

This challenge of daunting technology reminds me of when I ran with the bulls in Pamplona, Spain, in July 1997. It was over 20 years ago now, but I remember it like it was yesterday. One of the most vivid moments occurred after I ran down the narrow *via* through the ancient Jewish ghetto on the way to the arena with bulls in hot pursuit. Because that's when the real action begins.

After running with the bulls, you are in the arena at about seven o'clock in the morning — tired, hungover, and pumped full of adrenaline. And you look around, and there are thousands of screaming people, cheering that you made it into the arena.

But they are also cheering, because they want to see you wrestle baby bulls that weigh about 500 pounds, which is what comes next. As I looked to my left, I saw one of these bulls charging a guy dressed in the same white outfit with red scarf and bandana as I had on. As that bull was about to run him down, he covered his eyes. To no one's surprise, except likely his own, this did not make the bull go away.

He got trampled — and then he was carried off on a stretcher.

Technology is changing. And the future will bring a mix of good and ill. But the changes are coming whether we like them or not. There is simply no going back. You've been thrown out of the Garden of Eden; there is no going back.

And you can cover your eyes all you like and pretend it isn't happening, but you will get trampled too. And there may or may not be a stretcher waiting for you.

On the upside, there are not too many construction workers who bemoan the fact that building foundations are dug out with backhoes rather than by hand with shovels. Technology usually helps us, and as we saw in Chapter 2, the jobs in warehousing transportation and storage pay significantly more than all retail store jobs, except for auto sales, which I find to be a bit of a stretch to define as a retail sales job.

The best thing you can do to be futureproof is to accept that technology is changing and find ways to benefit from it. Use chatbots, learn new programs, and leverage the ability to publish in a highly democratized era of information and printing.

Of course, I'm not just giving armchair advice here. I have published numerous books on technology, and they have helped me become a trusted thought partner to some of the biggest corporations in the world. I can only make the recommendation to do the same in the hope that you benefit from it as well!

But don't forget about formal training.

Make sure to snag as many degrees and certificates as you can. If you aren't building your professional skills, they are surely at risk of suffering from atrophy. Structured learning is important, which is the reason I founded The Futurist Institute and created the Futurist and Long-Term Analyst — FLTA — certification program. It was with the single goal to help other people become futurists by training current and future leaders to incorporate new and emerging technology risks into their strategic planning.

Pulling Everything Together

FUTUREPROOF SUPPLY CHAIN

Thank you for reading this book on futureproof supply chain.

Everything from customer and vendor interfaces to transport and logistics as well as last mile delivery issues and inanimate demand in an IoT world will drive supply chain transformations, as well as the way in which companies operate, sell, and survive. Companies that take up the mantle of technological innovation will be futureproof.

They will survive and thrive.

But those companies that do not embrace the rapid changes will die on the vine. And the same is true of individuals. To be futureproof, you must embrace the future and honestly wrestle with the disruptions — both the massive opportunities and the devastating risks.

There is no way back. And you must push forward. But trust me, you'll want to!

Beyond emerging new technology risks and opportunities, there are a host of other challenges facing supply chain in the decade ahead. Developments in the economy, financial markets, and politics also have the ability to significantly impact companies' supply chains over the next decade.

These topics need to be considered and monitored. Having an approach to economic, financial, and political shocks is something that is best to prepare for before those risks come fully to fruition.

You don't have to have plans for all eventualities. That is wildly unreasonable, but the risk committee of your company — or at least the executives tasked with risk management — should be aware of the most risky dynamics that lie just ahead.

Further Learning

If you've enjoyed this book and want to learn more about becoming a futurist, and how to incorporate new and emerging technology risk into your strategic planning, I would recommend pursuing the Futurist and Long-Term Analyst (FLTA) training program that I created for The Futurist Institute. All of the details about the FLTA can be found at www.futuristinstitute.org.

Additionally, if risk management is a topic that is of significant interest, you can take my LinkedIn Learning course on *Finance Foundations: Risk Management*. Here is the link to that course: https://www.linkedin.com/learning/finance-foundations-risk-management.

The future will be made up of innovations and risks that happen slowly, and then all at once.

Knowledge is power, and now you have a roadmap of the greatest disruption risks I expect in the decade ahead. It is my wish that this book helps you and your company prepare for the future.

That it makes you futureproof!

ENDNOTES

Chapter 2

1. U.S. Bureau of the Census, E-Commerce Retail Sales [ECOMSA], retrieved from FRED, Federal Reserve Bank of St. Louis; https://fred.stlouisfed.org/series/ECOMSA, February 9, 2019.
2. U.S. Bureau of the Census, E-Commerce Retail Sales as a Percent of Total Sales [ECOMPCTSA], retrieved from FRED, Federal Reserve Bank of St. Louis; https://fred.stlouisfed.org/series/ECOMPCTSA, February 9, 2019.
3. U.S. Bureau of Labor Statistics, All Employees: Retail Trade: Department Stores (DISCONTINUED) [CES4245210001], retrieved from FRED, Federal Reserve Bank of St. Louis; https://fred.stlouisfed.org/series/CES4245210001, February 9, 2019.
4. U.S. Bureau of Labor Statistics, All Employees: Transportation and Warehousing: Warehousing and Storage [CES4349300001], retrieved from FRED, Federal Reserve Bank of St. Louis; https://fred.stlouisfed.org/series/CES4349300001, February 9, 2019.
5. U.S. Bureau of Labor Statistics, Retrieved from Bureau of Labor Statistics; https://www.bls.gov/oes/2017/may/oes412031.htm, February 9, 2019.
6. U.S. Bureau of Labor Statistics, Retrieved from Bureau of Labor Statistics; https://www.bls.gov/iag/tgs/iag493.htm, February 9, 2019.

Chapter 4

1. Chapter image from www.123rf.com.
2. Chapter image from www.123rf.com.

Chapter 5

1. Chapter image from www.123rf.com.
2. Chapter image from www.123rf.com.

Chapter 7

Chapter image from www.123rf.com.

Chapter 10

1. Krafcik, J. (October 10, 2018). "Where the Next 10 Million Milles Will Take Us." *Medium*. Retrieved from: https://medium.com/waymo/where-the-next-10-million-miles-will-take-us-de51bebb67d3, February 9, 2019.
2. Silver, D. (July 26, 2018). "Waymo Has the Most Autonomous Miles, By a Lot." *Forbes*. Retrieved from: https://www.forbes.com/sites/davidsilver/2018/07/26/waymo-has-the-most-autonomous-miles-by-a-lot/#62cf8d307ee5, February 9, 2019.
3. U.S. Federal Highway Administration, Moving 12-Month Total Vehicle Miles Traveled [M12MTVUSM227NFWA], retrieved from FRED, Federal Reserve Bank of St. Louis; https://fred.stlouisfed.org/series/M12MTVUSM227NFWA, February 9, 2019.
4. Image of Waymo truck and car from Waymo press kit.

Chapter 12

Chapter image from www.123rf.com.

Chapter 13

1. Desjardins, J. (August 6, 2015). "$60 Trillion of World Debt in One Visualization." Visual Capitalist. Retrieved February 11, 2017: http://www.visualcapitalist.com/60-trillion-of-world-debt-in-one-visualization/.

2. Mayer, J. (November 18, 2015). "The Social Security Façade." Retrieved February 11, 2017: http://www.usnews.com/opinion/economic-intelligence/2015/11/18/social-security-and-medicare-have-morphed-into-unsustainable-entitlements.

3. Image provided courtesy of The Heritage Foundation. Retrieved February 11, 2017: http://thf_media.s3.amazonaws.com/infographics/2014/10/BG-eliminate-waste-control-spending-chart-3_HIGHRES.jpg.

4. Twarog, S. (January 1997). "Heights and Living Standards in Germany, 1850-1939: The Case of Wurttemberg" as reprinted in *Health and Welfare During Industrialization*. Steckel, R. and F. Roderick eds. Chicago: University of Chicago Press, p. 315. Retrieved February 11, 2017: http://www.nber.org/chapters/c7434.pdf.

5. U.S. Social Security Administration. "Social Security History: Otto von Bismarck." Sourced from https://www.ssa.gov/history/ottob.html.

6. U.S. Social Security Administration. *Fast Facts and Figures About Social Security*, 2017, p.8. Retrieved on June 6, 2018: https://www.ssa.gov/policy/docs/chartbooks/fast_facts/.

Chapter 14

1. World Bank, Population Growth for the United States [SPPOPGROWUSA], retrieved from FRED, Federal Reserve Bank of St. Louis; https://fred.stlouisfed.org/series/SPPOPGROWUSA, June 5, 2018.

2. Last, J. (2013) *What to Expect, When No One's Expecting: America's Coming Demographic Disaster*. New York: Encounter Books., pp. 2-4.

3. Ibid., p. 3.

4. Last (2013), p. 109.

5. Social Security Administration. Retrieved February 11, 2017, from https://www.ssa.gov/history/ratios.html Last (2013) also uses a similar table in his book on p. 108.

6. Last (2013), p. 107.

7. U.S. Internal Revenue Service. Retrieved from https://www.irs.gov/businesses/small-businesses-self-employed/self-employment-tax-social-security-and-medicare-taxes.

8. Pew Research Center. (October 22, 2015). Retrieved February 19, 2017: http://www.pewsocialtrends.org/2015/10/22/three-in-ten-u-s-jobs-are-held-by-the-self-employed-and-the-workers-they-hire/.

9. Ibid.

Chapter 16

1. "Transaction Speeds: How Do Cryptocurrencies Stack Up to Visa or PayPal?" (10 January 2018). howmuch.net. Retrieved on 24 August, 2018, from https://howmuch.net/sources/crypto-transaction-speeds-compared.

ABOUT THE AUTHOR

Jason Schenker is the President of Prestige Economics and the world's top-ranked financial market futurist. Bloomberg News has ranked Mr. Schenker one of the most accurate forecasters in the world in 43 different categories since 2011, including #1 in the world in 25 categories for his forecasts of the Euro, the Pound, the Swiss Franc, the Chinese RMB, crude oil prices, natural gas prices, gold prices, industrial metals prices, agricultural prices, U.S. non-farm payrolls, and U.S. new home sales.

Mr. Schenker has written 12 books and edited two almanacs. Five of his books have been #1 Best Sellers on Amazon, including *Commodity Prices 101*, *Recession-Proof*, *Electing Recession*, *Quantum: Computing Nouveau*, and *Jobs for Robots*. He also edited the #1 Best Seller *The Robot and Automation Almanac - 2018* as well as the 2019 edition of the almanac. Mr. Schenker is also a columnist for *Bloomberg Opinion*. He has appeared as a guest and guest host on Bloomberg Television as well as a guest on CNBC. He is frequently quoted in the press, including *The Wall Street Journal*, *The New York Times*, and *The Financial Times*.

Prior to founding Prestige Economics, Mr. Schenker worked for McKinsey & Company as a Risk Specialist, where he directed trading and risk initiatives on six continents. Before joining McKinsey, Mr. Schenker worked for Wachovia as an Economist.

Mr. Schenker holds a Master's in Applied Economics from UNC Greensboro, a Master's in Negotiation from CSU Dominguez Hills, a Master's in German from UNC Chapel Hill, and a Bachelor's with distinction in History and German from The University of Virginia. He also holds a certificate in FinTech from MIT, an executive certificate in Supply Chain Management from MIT, a graduate certificate in Professional Development from UNC, a certificate in Negotiation from Harvard Law School, and a certificate in Cybersecurity from Carnegie Mellon University.

Mr. Schenker holds the professional designations ERP® (Energy Risk Professional), CMT® (Chartered Market Technician), CVA® (Certified Valuation Analyst), CFP® (Certified Financial Planner), and FLTA™ (Certified Futurist and Long-Term Analyst). Mr. Schenker is also an instructor for LinkedIn Learning. His courses include Financial Risk Management, Recession-Proof Strategies, Audit and Due Diligence, and a weekly Economic Indicator Series.

Mr. Schenker is a member of the Texas Business Leadership Council, the only CEO-based public policy research organization in Texas, with a limited membership of 100 CEOs and Presidents. He is also a member of the 2018 Director class of the Texas Lyceum, a non-partisan, nonprofit that fosters business and policy dialogue on important U.S. and Texas issues. He is also on the Texas Lyceum Executive Committee as the VP of Technology.

Mr. Schenker is an active executive in FinTech. He has been a member of the Central Texas Angel Network and is currently the Executive Director of the Texas Blockchain Association. He is also a member of the National Association of Corporate Directors as well as an NACD Board Governance Fellow.

In October 2016, Mr. Schenker founded The Futurist Institute to help analysts, strategists, and economists become futurists through a training and certification program. Participants can earn the FLTA — Certified Futurist and Long-Term Analyst designation.

Mr. Schenker was ranked one of the top 100 most influential financial advisors in the world by Investopedia in June 2018.

For more information about Jason Schenker:
www.jasonschenker.com

For more information about The Futurist Institute:
www.futuristinstitute.org

For more information about Prestige Economics:
www.prestigeeconomics.com

TOP FORECASTER ACCURACY RANKINGS

Prestige Economics has been recognized as the most accurate independent commodity and financial market research firm in the world. As the only forecaster for Prestige Economics, Jason Schenker is very proud that Bloomberg News has ranked him a top forecaster in 43 different categories since 2011, including #1 in the world in 25 different forecast categories.

Mr. Schenker has been top ranked as a forecaster of economic indicators, energy prices, metals prices, agricultural prices, and foreign exchange rates.

ECONOMIC TOP RANKINGS
#1 Non-Farm Payroll Forecaster in the World
#1 New Home Sales Forecaster in the World
#2 U.S. Unemployment Rate Forecaster in the World
#3 Durable Goods Orders Forecaster in the World
#6 Consumer Confidence Forecaster in the World
#7 ISM Manufacturing Index Forecaster in the World
#7 U.S. Housing Start Forecaster in the World

ENERGY PRICE TOP RANKINGS

#1 WTI Crude Oil Price Forecaster in the World

#1 Brent Crude Oil Price Forecaster in the World

#1 Henry Hub Natural Gas Price Forecaster in the World

METALS PRICE TOP RANKINGS

#1 Gold Price Forecaster in the World

#1 Platinum Price Forecaster in the World

#1 Palladium Price Forecaster in the World

#1 Industrial Metals Price Forecaster in the World

#1 Copper Price Forecaster in the World

#1 Aluminum Price Forecaster in the World

#1 Nickel Price Forecaster in the World

#1 Tin Price Forecaster in the World

#1 Zinc Price Forecaster in the World

#2 Precious Metals Price Forecaster in the World

#2 Silver Price Forecaster in the World

#2 Lead Price Forecaster in the World

#2 Iron Ore Forecaster in the World

AGRICULTURAL PRICE TOP RANKINGS

#1 Coffee Price Forecaster in the World

#1 Cotton Price Forecaster in the World

#1 Sugar Price Forecaster in the World

#1 Soybean Price Forecaster in the World

FOREIGN EXCHANGE TOP RANKINGS

#1 Euro Forecaster in the World

#1 British Pound Forecaster in the World

#1 Swiss Franc Forecaster in the World

#1 Chinese RMB Forecaster in the World

#1 Russian Ruble Forecaster in the World

#1 Brazilian Real Forecaster in the World

#2 Turkish Lira Forecaster in the World

#3 Major Currency Forecaster in the World

#3 Canadian Dollar Forecaster in the World

#4 Japanese Yen Forecaster in the World

#5 Australian Dollar Forecaster in the World

#7 Mexican Peso Forecaster in the World

#1 EURCHF Forecaster in the World

#2 EURJPY Forecaster in the World

#2 EURGBP Forecaster in the World

#2 EURRUB Forecaster in the World

ABOUT THE PUBLISHER

Prestige Professional Publishing LLC was founded in 2011 to produce insightful and timely professional reference books. We are registered with the Library of Congress.

Published Titles

Be the Shredder, Not the Shred

Commodity Prices 101

Electing Recession

Financial Risk Management Fundamentals

Futureproof Supply Chain

A Gentle Introduction to Audit and Due Diligence

Jobs for Robots

Midterm Economics

The Promise of Blockchain

Quantum: Computing Nouveau

Robot-Proof Yourself

The Robot and Automation Almanac — 2018

The Robot and Automation Almanac — 2019

Future Titles

The Fog of Data

Spikes: Growth Hacking Leadership

The Robot and Automation Almanac: 2019 is a collection of essays by robot and automation experts, executives, and investors on the big trends to watch for in automation, AI, and robotics in 2019. *The Robot and Automation Almanac: 2019* was compiled by The Futurist Institute and published by Prestige Professional Publishing in December 2018.

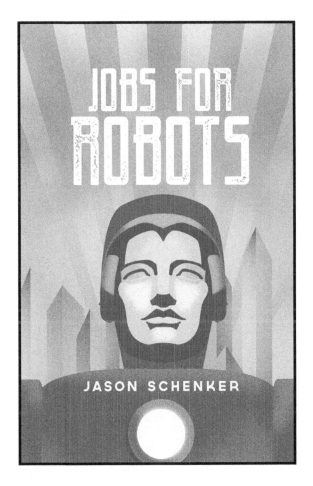

Jobs for Robots provides an in-depth look at the future of automation and robots, with a focus on the opportunities as well as the risks ahead. Job creation in coming years will be extremely strong for the kind of workers that do not require payroll taxes, health care, or vacation: robots. *Jobs for Robots* was published in February 2017. This book has been a #1 Best Seller on Amazon.

Robot-Proof Yourself offers a number of practical professional recommendations for how to be robot-proof in the coming era of professional, economic, and financial disruptions. Robots and automation are set to advance, but individuals have a chance to benefit from the coming changes. *Robot-Proof Yourself* was released in December 2017.

Spikes: Growth Hacking Leadership presents proactive strategies to help individuals advance rapidly in their professional careers by hacking the system. This book is slated to be published in early 2019 by Prestige Professional Publishing.

DISCLAIMER

FROM THE AUTHOR

The following disclaimer applies to any content in this book:

This book is commentary intended for general information use only and is not investment advice. Jason Schenker does not make recommendations on any specific or general investments, investment types, asset classes, non-regulated markets, specific equities, bonds, or other investment vehicles. Jason Schenker does not guarantee the completeness or accuracy of analyses and statements in this book, nor does Jason Schenker assume any liability for any losses that may result from the reliance by any person or entity on this information. Opinions, forecasts, and information are subject to change without notice. This book does not represent a solicitation or offer of financial or advisory services or products; this book is only market commentary intended and written for general information use only. This book does not constitute investment advice. All links were correct and active at the time this book was published.

DISCLAIMER

FROM THE PUBLISHER

The following disclaimer applies to any content in this book:

This book is commentary intended for general information use only and is not investment advice. Prestige Professional Publishing LLC does not make recommendations on any specific or general investments, investment types, asset classes, non-regulated markets, specific equities, bonds, or other investment vehicles. Prestige Professional Publishing LLC does not guarantee the completeness or accuracy of analyses and statements in this book, nor does Prestige Professional Publishing LLC assume any liability for any losses that may result from the reliance by any person or entity on this information. Opinions, forecasts, and information are subject to change without notice. This book does not represent a solicitation or offer of financial or advisory services or products; this book is only market commentary intended and written for general information use only. This book does not constitute investment advice. All links were correct and active at the time this book was published.

Prestige Professional Publishing LLC

7101 Fig Vine Cove

Austin, Texas 78750

www.prestigeprofessionalpublishing.com

ISBN: 978-1-946197-26-9 *Paperback*
      978-1-946197-24-5 *Ebook*